THE WRIGHTSMAN GALLERIES
FOR FRENCH DECORATIVE ARTS
The Metropolitan Museum of Art

THE WRIGHTSMAN GALLERIES FOR FRENCH DECORATIVE ARTS

The Metropolitan Museum of Art

Daniëlle Kisluk-Grosheide and Jeffrey Munger

The Metropolitan Museum of Art, New York

Yale University Press, New Haven and London

This publication is made possible by the Marie-Josée and Henry R. Kravis Foundation.

Published by The Metropolitan Museum of Art, New York

Gwen Roginsky, General Manager of Publications

Margaret Rennolds Chace, Managing Editor

Peter Antony, Chief Production Manager

Ellyn Childs Allison, Editor

Bruce Campbell, Designer

Robert Weisberg, Assistant Managing Editor

Bonnie Laessig, Production Manager

Unless otherwise specified, all photographs were supplied by the owners of the works of art, who hold the copyright thereto, and are reproduced with permission. We have made every effort to obtain permissions for all copyright-protected images. If you have copyright-protected work in this publication and you have not given us permission, please contact the Metropolitan Museum's Editorial Department. Photographs of works in the Metropolitan Museum's collection are by the Photograph Studio, The Metropolitan Museum of Art; new photography is by Joseph Coscia Jr., Katherine Dahab, and Peter Zeray. Additional photograph credits appear on p. 259.

Separations by Professional Graphics, Inc., Rockford, Illinois

Printed and bound by Mondadori Printing S.p.A., Verona, Italy

Front of jacket/cover: The Cabris Room (no. 6)

Back of jacket/cover: The Bordeaux Room (no. 9)

Frontispiece: Detail of an ivory vase with gilt-bronze mounts (no. 68)

Page v: Detail of a secretary on stand (no. 47)

Page x: Detail of a covered vase (no. 102)

Page 260: Detail of a secretary on stand (no. 32)

Cataloging-in-Publication Data is available from the Library of Congress.

ISBN 978-1-58839-366-1 (hc: The Metropolitan Museum of Art)

ISBN 978-1-58839-367-8 (pbk: The Metropolitan Museum of Art)

ISBN 978-0-300-15520-4 (hc: Yale University Press)

TO JAYNE WRIGHTSMAN

Contents

Director's Foreword

The extraordinary contributions made to the Metropolitan by Mr. and Mrs. Charles Wrightsman can be seen and admired throughout the Museum. Those contributions, which include superb decorative objects, sculpture, paintings, and drawings, given over a period of six decades to various curatorial departments, have greatly enriched our holdings. Many endowed galleries are also testimony to their generosity.

It is no secret that of all the rooms in the Museum, the Wrightsman Galleries for French Decorative Arts hold a special place in Jayne Wrightsman's heart. The present handbook celebrates the recent renewal of those galleries, which, once again, was funded by this exceptional donor. The distillation of many years of curatorial research, the book provides our visitors with concise information on the Wrightsman period rooms and galleries as well as a selection of the objects so beautifully displayed in them.

My predecessor, Philippe de Montebello, and I salute Henry and Marie-Josée Kravis for so generously making this book possible. We share their deep affection and admiration for Jayne Wrightsman, whose passionate commitment to French decorative arts has for many years guided and inspired this Museum.

Thomas P. Campbell
Director
The Metropolitan Museum of Art

Preface

In 2006–7 an eighteen-month campaign of research, design, conservation, and renovation brought new life to the Metropolitan Museum's famed Wrightsman Galleries. These period rooms and galleries house one of the finest collections in the world of French eighteenth-century decorative arts. The works were acquired throughout the course of the Museum's history as gifts and bequests from many donors or purchased through various funds. Most generous of all the donors were Mr. and Mrs. Charles Wrightsman. Their idea of displaying the furnishings within spaces bounded by wall paneling from historic houses—thus representing specific moments of interior decoration—underlies the character of the galleries, from their first installation to this latest renewal.

In the first decades of the twentieth century, American museums devoted considerable space to the high moments of French, English, Italian, and American interior decor. By the 1960s and 1970s, when the Wrightsmans, advised by curator James Parker, focused their attention and resources on the project, the Museum was able to coordinate a series of existing rooms and connecting galleries to elucidate changes in style from the late seventeenth century to the late eighteenth century.

The recent renovation has brought a fresh interpretation to the Wrightsman rooms. Knowledge gleaned from archival research guided the rearrangement and refurbishment of objects, and advances in lighting technology were used to achieve a more subtle and varied illumination. These efforts to conserve and preserve the rooms and their contents for the future reflect a new wave of interest in such historical displays, to which this Museum's American Wing as well as institutions in London and Paris are also enthusiastically responding. The continued relevance and interest of period rooms for today's visitors are assured.

This handbook to the Wrightsman Galleries is designed to answer the questions of visitors impressed by the beauty of the furnishings and the harmony they achieve with their surroundings. The authors, Daniëlle Kisluk-Grosheide and Jeffrey Munger—two curators who were closely involved in the 2006–7 reinstallation—rethought the concept of the first guidebook (1979), which was organized by room, and decided to adopt a more flexible ordering by artistic medium. Following accounts of the history of each room's wall paneling are sections on such subjects as furniture, gilt bronze, textiles, porcelain, silverware, and portraits. This new approach helps the reader to follow changes of style within each area of interest and offers the curators more freedom to vary the display in each room without upsetting its relation to the text. Quotations from contemporary letters, diaries, and travel journals sharpen our perception of the society that moved through these spaces and sat in these chairs and our appreciation of how these surroundings were viewed in the eighteenth century. We are indebted to the Marie-Josée and Henry R. Kravis Foundation, whose directors, through admiration and affection for Jayne Wrightsman, have made this publication possible.

A small army of specialists joined forces in 2006 to renovate the Wrightsman Galleries. Experts in lighting, construction, and art installation worked beside staff of the Metropolitan's Department of Objects Conservation. The authors of this handbook joined Curator Melinda Watt and me in supervising curatorial decisions governing display. Conservators and scientists Drew Anderson, Mechthild Baumeister, Lawrence Becker, Linda Borsch, Nancy Britton, Marco Leona, Pascale Patris, Lisa Pilosi, Adriana Rizzo, and Jack Soultanian Jr. undertook scientific testing and research as well as supervised teams of dedicated colleagues. From London, Patrick Kinmonth contributed critical advice on the arrangement of the rooms, assisted by Museum designer Michael Langley. Larry French and his colleagues at the San Francisco–based firm of Auerbach Glasow French devised the lighting, for which they received the 2009 International Association of Lighting Designers Award of Excellence.

No project in the Museum could proceed without the support of its director. Philippe de Montebello's enthusiasm for French art ensured that the reinstallation would be a significant achievement; his successor, Thomas P. Campbell, once a member of the European Sculpture and Decorative Arts Department, has continued to champion the Wrightsman Galleries and this publication.

The animating spirit of all these endeavors has been Jayne Wrightsman's passion for French decorative arts. Her keen eye and deep knowledge of the field, combined with an unfailing generosity, have made it possible to bring the presentation of the collections—in the galleries that bear her name and in this book—to the peak of perfection.

Ian Wardropper
Iris and B. Gerald Cantor Chairman
European Sculpture and Decorative Arts

Acknowledgments

Every publication is the result of a collaborative effort, and this handbook is no exception. We thank our former and current directors, Philippe de Montebello and Thomas P. Campbell, for their support of this volume. We are most grateful for the encouragement and valuable assistance of our colleagues in the Department of European Sculpture and Decorative Arts who helped us in numerous ways: Ian Wardropper, Alisa Chiles, Elizabeth A. H. Cleland, Paola D'Agostino, James David Draper, Marva Harvey, the late Robert Kaufmann, Wolfram Koeppe, Erin E. Pick, Melissa Smith, Denny Stone, Clare Vincent, Melinda Watt, and especially also our departmental technicians, Juan Stacy and Bedel Tiscareño. We owe a special word of thanks to Elizabeth L. Berszinn and Janice Barnard, who volunteered their time and read the manuscript in various stages of completion.

We express our appreciation to Kenneth Soehner and the staff of the Thomas J. Watson Library for their assistance in locating missing volumes and ordering countless interlibrary loans. In the Department of Objects Conservation we are indebted to Lawrence Becker, Mechthild Baumeister, Linda Borsch, Nancy C. Britton, Pascale Patris, and Wendy Walker. Our gratitude also extends to the Department of Textile Conservation, especially to Florica Zaharia and Cristina B. Carr, to Michael Langley in the Special Exhibitions, Gallery Installations, and Design Department, and to Neal Stimler in the Image Library.

Beautiful images and illuminating details of the featured objects are essential in a book of this nature. We thank Barbara Bridgers and the staff of the Photograph Studio, especially Einar Brendalen, Robert Goldman, Thomas Ling, and Mark Morosse. Our debt to Joseph Coscia Jr., chief photographer of the numerous splendid images specially taken for this book, sometimes under difficult circumstances, is immeasurable. Additional images are the work of Peter Zeray and Katherine Dahab, to whom we are grateful as well.

We extend our profound thanks to the Editorial Department for the editing, design, and production of this book. We are grateful to the late John P. O'Neill, who served until recently as Publisher and Editor in Chief, Peter Antony, Margaret R. Chace, Bonnie Laessig, Gwen Roginsky, Jane S. Tai, and Robert Weisberg. The clear layout and elegant design of the volume were the work of Bruce Campbell. Noteworthy also are Jayne Kuchna's tireless efforts, which helped make the bibliography and footnotes as perfect and complete as possible. Elaine Luthy was most thorough in compiling the index. We owe an enormous debt to Ellyn Childs Allison, our invaluable editor, who prepared the manuscript for production, despite numerous distractions, with patience, superb organization, and, most importantly, unfailing good humor. Finally, the authors are grateful to Eugene J. and Sylvester Kisluk, and to Rob Whitman for their love and encouragement throughout the endeavor.

Daniëlle Kisluk-Grosheide and Jeffrey Munger

Note to the Reader

All the works of art featured in this book are in the permanent collection of The Metropolitan Museum of Art. Information about them in the entry headings is always presented in the same sequence. The omission of any line of information, such as the name of the maker, indicates that the information is not available or that the line is not applicable. Sometimes only one of several identical works in the Museum's collection—for example, a pair of candlesticks or a trio of chairs—is illustrated. In such cases, the heading of the entry clarifies that fact and the accession numbers of all the items in the set are given.

Birth and death dates of makers, designers, and others who helped create the objects are given in the entry headings when they are known. Life dates for other significant persons are included in the introduction and entries at the first time of mention and are repeated in the index.

Dimensions are given with the height preceding the width and the width preceding the depth. Measurements are given in centimeters and to the nearest eighth of an inch or the nearest sixteenth of an inch if the object is very small. All dimensions are maximum unless otherwise noted.

The author of the introduction to each section is also the author of the entries in that section, except in "Gilt Bronze and Mounted Porcelain." There, the author's initials appear at the end of each entry.

Bibliographical references are cited in the text in abbreviated form. The corresponding full citations are given in the bibliography.

THE WRIGHTSMAN GALLERIES
FOR FRENCH DECORATIVE ARTS

The Metropolitan Museum of Art

INTRODUCTION

DANIËLLE KISLUK-GROSHEIDE

Flanked by the Carroll and Milton Petrie European Sculpture Court on the south side and the Medieval Hall on the north side, the Wrightsman Galleries for French Decorative Arts are located on the Metropolitan Museum's main floor, occupying an area measuring an impressive 12,000 square feet (fig. 1). Devoted to the decorative arts of seventeenth- and especially eighteenth-century France, they comprise twelve galleries, including eight paneled rooms, for the display of the Museum's magnificent holdings of furniture, Savonnerie carpets, gilt bronze, Sèvres porcelain, silver, and gold boxes. The presentation of these artworks in period-room settings and adjacent spaces conjures up the formal etiquette of the French court and daily life in the residences of the nobility during the ancien régime. The paneling (*boiseries*) of the Morgan Alcove, also called the Louis XV Room, and of the Varengeville and Paar rooms are fine expressions of the Rococo style, which dominated Europe during the reign of Louis XV (r. 1715–74). Those in the Tessé, Cabris, Lauzun, Bordeaux, and Crillon rooms, as well as the paneled front of a shop from the Île Saint-Louis, beautifully illustrate the return to classicism under Louis XVI (r. 1774–92). Ever since the acquisition in 1963 of the paneling from the Hôtel de Varengeville and the Palais Paar with funds given by Mr. and Mrs. Charles Wrightsman, all these rooms have borne the Wrightsmans' name. Their extraordinary generosity to the Museum also made possible the renovation of existing French galleries as well as the installation of additional period rooms. Numerous pieces of royal furniture, porcelain, and other furnishings, gifts of Mr. and Mrs. Wrightsman, have enriched the Museum's already strong collections of French decorative arts, making them unrivaled outside Europe. In the galleries, these Wrightsman objects are displayed together with important artworks from other donors, such as J. Pierpont Morgan, Catherine D. Wentworth, Jules S. Bache, and the Samuel H. Kress Foundation.

The Wrightsman Galleries are a testimony to the splendor, elegance, and luxury of the French interior during the ancien régime. These qualities impressed and delighted many contemporary visitors to France but were not admired by all. John Adams (1735–1826), for instance, who was to serve as the second president of the United States, commented in 1778 in a letter to his wife on the magnificence of French public buildings and private houses alike, concluding, "But what is all this to me? I receive but little pleasure in beholding all these things, because I cannot but consider them as bagatelles. . . . I cannot help suspecting that the more elegance, the less virtue, in all times and countries."[1]

Only one book on the Wrightsman Galleries has preceded this one. Published in 1979, it was coauthored by James Parker (1924–2001), who oversaw the installation of the French rooms during his long tenure as curator in the Department of European Sculpture and Decorative Arts, and Clare Le Corbeiller (1931–2003), who was for many years in charge of the Museum's collections of Continental porcelain and silver. This useful volume has become a collector's item, since it was never reprinted or revised. Subsequent additions to the collections, new scholarly discoveries, and changes that have taken place in the French galleries since 1979 have never been published. Honoring the continued generosity of Mrs. Jayne Wrightsman and celebrating the recent important renovations, the Henry and Marie-Josée Kravis Foundation has made the publication of this new handbook possible.

In a departure from the earlier volume, which was organized by room, this book is divided into sections devoted to the different categories of furnishings that fill the rooms: the wood paneling and a selection of the furniture,

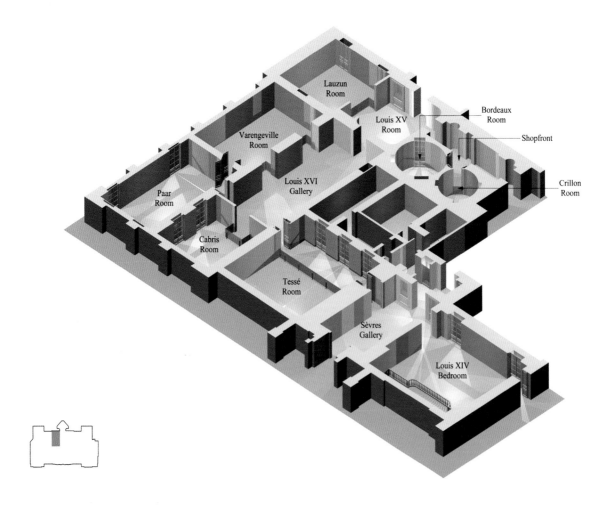

Fig. 1. The Wrightsman Galleries for French Decorative Arts, 2009. Plan by Michael Langley.

porcelain, gilt bronze, fireplaces and their equipment, textiles, portraits, silver, and gold boxes. This presentation is less restrictive and will not be outdated by occasional changes in the galleries, where the display is not meant to be static. Also, when artworks are grouped by material, it is easier to observe the evolving style and decoration in period paneling or furniture, for instance, and to understand better how changes in dining practices affected the shapes and embellishment of table silver and porcelain. In order to make the text livelier and to place the objects in a contemporary light, seventeenth- and eighteenth-century letters, diaries, and travel journals are cited where appropriate.

THE FRENCH GALLERIES, 1910–60

The Metropolitan Museum's strength in French decorative arts, which dates back to its early years, is in great part due to a generous gift from J. Pierpont Morgan (1837–1913). In 1907 Morgan presented the institution with a large collection of French eighteenth-century woodwork, paneling, furniture, and gilt bronze that had been assembled by Georges Hoentschel (1855–1915), a Parisian architect, decorator, and ceramist. Hoentschel had also amassed a collection of medieval art, and both collections were installed in a warehouse at 58, boulevard Flandrin that had been specially built for this purpose.

Morgan, the financier and philanthropist who became a Museum trustee in 1888 and who served as its fourth president, had acquired both collections in 1906 for the impressive sum of four million French francs. Whereas the eighteenth-century decorative arts were presented outright to the Museum, "primarily for the benefit of the craftsmen and designers," the medieval holdings were initially given on loan.[2] By May of the following year, 364 packing cases containing the entire Hoentschel collection were stored in the Museum's basement.[3] This splendid gift led not only to the creation of a special department for decorative arts, the predecessor of the Department of European Sculpture and Decorative Arts as it is presently known, but also to the appointment of William R. Valentiner (1880–1958) as its first curator. He was "given the control . . . of all sections of the Museum which come under the heading of Decorative Art, with the exception of the Chinese and Japanese collections."[4] The construction of a wing to display the Hoentschel collection also ensued.[5] Designed by the architectural firm of McKim, Mead and White, this addition, called the Wing of Decorative Arts, was opened to the public on March 15, 1910. With its large central hall surrounded by two floors of smaller rooms, the new building comprised twenty-five galleries devoted largely to French decorative arts dating from the twelfth to the nineteenth century. Those galleries were never meant to be reserved for the Hoentschel collection, however; Morgan himself had indicated that "the objects shall be placed upon the walls with such freedom of spacing that other things of a similar character may be hung among them as they accumulate."[6] Today the ground floor of this wing houses the Museum's holdings of arms and armor, while musical instruments are displayed upstairs.

Since the architect Charles F. McKim (1847–1909) had seen the Hoentschel collection as it was installed almost as a private museum in Paris and was familiar with the Musée des Arts Décoratifs, which had been recently established in that city as well, it is not surprising that the Metropolitan's arrangement derived inspiration from both galleries. However, the Pavillon de Marsan and the rue de Rivoli wing of the Louvre—home to the Musée des Arts Décoratifs since its opening in 1905—were not originally intended as an art museum. By contrast, the

Fig. 2. Gallery in the Morgan Wing, ca. 1910, with a display of woodwork and furniture of the Louis XIV and Régence periods.

new wing at the Metropolitan was erected for that purpose and was considered superior to the French museum in its lighting and ceiling heights.[7] Special attention was also given to the ventilation system to protect the artworks from changes in temperature and humidity.

Displaying a variety of carved woodwork and paneling—mostly anonymous fragments—as well as mantelpieces and decorative paintings hung on the walls, and with furniture positioned on platforms below them, the collection was organized in a chronological sequence. The seven rooms devoted to French art from the seventeenth and eighteenth centuries reflected the taste prevailing during the reigns of the different kings (see fig. 2).[8] Following the opening, an article in the New York Times poetically described the French galleries:

Passing through the rooms devoted to these relics of the three Louis reigns, noting here a pair of doors from the Château of Marly-le-roi, there, a mirror from the Tuileries, in one corner a door decorated by Huet's silvery harmonies, and everywhere bagatelles made by workmen who took their craft more seriously than anything else was taken in that pleasure-loving society, we get an impression that no books could provide for us and that no individual example could awaken[,] a dreamlike vision of an old grace and elegance, an

Fig. 3. Walter Gay, *The Morgan Alcove Installed in the Morgan Wing of The Metropolitan Museum of Art*, ca. 1911. Oil on canvas, 25½ × 21 in. (64.8 × 53.3 cm). Saint Louis Art Museum, Museum Purchase (27:1926).

Fig. 4. Eighteenth-century shopfront from the Île Saint-Louis, Paris, installed in the Morgan Wing, 1920.

old amorous gayety and frivolity, a dance of loves and nymphs with pretty powdered heads and flowered silken bodices, which is not less lovely for the dim haze of time through which we behold it.[9]

Among the features of the new wing was some early eighteenth-century paneling. Although the woodwork has no known provenance, it must once have graced the walls of an important residence, since its rounded corner panels are richly decorated with carved and gilded trophies representing various occupations symbolic of the four seasons. In all probability, it was originally part of a larger room, but the *boiserie* was assembled at the Museum as an alcove, following the arrangement that it had been given at the boulevard Flandrin as part of the Hoentschel collection. The first installation of this so-called Morgan Alcove in New York became the subject of a painting (fig. 3) by the American artist Walter Gay (1856–1937).[10]

After J. Pierpont Morgan's death, his son, J. P. (Jack) Morgan Jr. (1867–1943), made two gifts to the Museum: in 1916 the medieval works from the Hoentschel collection and the following year some three thousand objects from his father's private collection, artworks that had been part of the Morgan Loan Exhibition held at the Museum in

1914–16. The decorative arts wing, where the Hoentschel collection had been shown since 1910, would thereafter be devoted to the permanent display of artworks given to the Metropolitan Museum by both the elder and the younger Morgan. Officially designated the Pierpont Morgan Wing, it reopened, following reinstallation, on June 11, 1918.[11]

One of the new purchases for these galleries was the late eighteenth-century facade of a small emporium formerly on the Île Saint-Louis, thought to be the only extant shopfront of the period in Paris (fig. 4). It was bought with funds provided by Jack Morgan, and immediately following its acquisition Joseph Breck (1885–1933), who had succeeded Valentiner as curator of the Department of Decorative Arts in 1917, wrote to the donor: "I am sure it will be very effective when installed in the Morgan Wing. It is certain to be popular as it has 'human interest' which can be increased by using the shop windows as show cases for some of the French faience in the Morgan Collection."[12]

Rich and varied as the Hoentschel and Morgan collections were in woodwork and paneling, they did not include complete rooms. This was clearly considered to be a shortcoming. Assistant Curator Meyric R. Rogers (1893–1957) observed in the *Bulletin of The Metropolitan*

Museum of Art for April 1921 that the absence of rooms was "one of the major reasons for the disfavor in which the art of mid-eighteenth century France is held by many who know it only through scattered examples, having lacked the opportunity of seeing, as it were, a complete design unit."[13] For this reason Rogers felt that "every piece of decorative art to gain its full value should be seen only in its proper setting, in the place for which it was originally designed and in surroundings created by the same artistic impulse."[14] The perceived need to show objects in a suitable environment was partly satisfied through the acquisition in 1920 of the *boiserie* from a room dating to about 1740–50. Jack Morgan wrote to Edward Robinson (1858–1931), then the Museum's director: "Mr. Breck has just been able to find in Paris, the complete paneling—with mantel and mirrors—of a room of the period of Louis XVth. This would make so complete a setting for specimen furniture of the time now forming part of the Hoentschel collection in the Morgan wing, that I desire to present it to the Metropolitan Museum of Art for such use."[15] The paneling came from a house on the rue Thorigny, Paris, believed to have been owned by Madame de Pompadour. Stripped for the Museum of its paint layers in order to bring out the quality of the carving, this Rococo woodwork was installed in a three-sided arrangement on the second floor of the Morgan Wing (fig. 5).[16] The room, originally a bedchamber with alcove, was furnished at the Museum with objects in the same style

and had as a result more "the appearance of a salon."[17] It was felt that this transformation did not contradict the spirit of the design, since the bedroom at that period was often used as a reception room. Rogers wrote in *The Pierpont Morgan Wing: A Handbook* that this kind of arrangement demonstrated the essential harmony existing between the "rather flamboyant lines of the Louis XV furniture and its surroundings. They were made to be seen together and neither appears to advantage without the other. Neglect of this principle and failure to provide a proper setting have led to an almost total misunderstanding of this style outside of France."[18] Composed of eighteenth-century elements to form a sympathetic background for a selection of furniture and decorative objects, the first French period room at the Metropolitan Museum was clearly more an evocation than an actual reconstitution of a specific historic room.[19]

This Rococo interior was followed not long afterward by three Neoclassical rooms: a salon, library, and bedchamber (fig. 6), all from the Hôtel Gaulin, in Dijon. These rooms, also the gifts of Jack Morgan, were installed leading into one another (*en enfilade*) according to their original layout and were completed with furnishings of the same period. Curators Breck and Rogers observed in the Museum *Bulletin* for December 1923 that "since most of the woodwork exhibited in the Morgan Wing is of fragmentary character, these *boiseries*, as complete ensembles illustrating the rich interior decoration of

Fig. 5. Paneled room from the rue Thorigny, Paris, installed in the Morgan Wing, 1923–53. Collotype by Max Jaffé, Vienna.

Fig. 6. Bedroom from the Hôtel Gaulin, Dijon, installed in the Morgan Wing, 1923–53. Collotype by Max Jaffé, Vienna.

the eighteenth century. . . . are particularly welcome accessions."[20]

The French period rooms remained on display in the Morgan Wing until 1953, when the decorative arts collections were transferred to a different part of the Museum and moved to specially renovated galleries on the first and ground floor of the original building. These major alterations led to the deinstallation and subsequent deaccessioning of the four period rooms.[21] Other paneling, displaying a higher level of quality in its carved or painted decorations, that had been acquired since the opening of the Morgan Wing replaced them. Neoclassicism reigned in those newly created interiors, all dating to the second half of the eighteenth century. The woodwork from a salon formerly in the Hôtel de Tessé, at 1, quai Voltaire, Paris (fig. 7), was considered to be "among the most distinguished *boiseries* ever to leave France."[22] It was the gift of Therese Kuhn Straus, widow of Herbert N. Straus, an heir to the Macy's department-store fortune. In 1943, the year after the arrival of the first salon, Mrs. Straus presented the Museum with a second—a charming circular room from a private residence in Bordeaux (fig. 8). These and other paneled rooms had been acquired for the New York mansion at 9 East Seventy-first Street that was built for Mr. and Mrs. Straus in a French Neoclassical style by the society architect Horace Trumbauer (1868–1938).[23] The house was left unfinished at the time of Mr. Straus's untimely death in 1933, and Mrs. Straus never moved in. Édouard Hitau, director of the New York office of the French decorating firm Alavoine, had

Fig. 7. The Tessé Room in 1954.

Fig. 8. The Bordeaux Room in 1954.

adjusted these two Louis XVI–style interiors for use as a drawing room and small circular reception room; they had not, however, been installed in the Straus residence. Hitau was later involved with the reconfiguration of the paneled rooms for the Museum. At that time an attempt was made to restore them as much as possible to their original, eighteenth-century dimensions and layout.

The third room to be incorporated in the new decorative arts galleries was a polyhedral mirrored boudoir, formerly at the Hôtel de Crillon on the place de la Concorde, Paris (fig. 9). It was made for Louis-Marie-Augustin, duc d'Aumont (1709–1782), a celebrated collector during the late eighteenth century. Based on designs by the architect Pierre-Adrien Pâris (1747–1819), the painted paneling displays lovely arabesque motifs and was the gift in 1944 of Susan Dwight Bliss (1882–1966). The room had been purchased in 1905 by her mother, Jeanette Dwight Bliss (d. 1924), widow of the prominent banker George T. Bliss, directly from the Hôtel de Crillon. It was to be incorporated in the New York mansion, then under construction, designed for her by the architects George Lewis Heins (1860–1907) and Christopher Grant Lafarge (1862–1938) at 9 East Sixty-eighth Street (fig. 10).

Since none of these paneled rooms arrived with their ceilings or cornices intact, they received modern replacements at the Museum. Although the floors, composed of oak squares known as *parquet de Versailles*, date to the eighteenth century, they were originally not part of the same buildings. In their new setting, these rooms became the repositories of significant pieces of French furniture already in the Museum's collections. Much of the fragmentary woodwork formerly on display in the Morgan Wing was now sent to storage, and needlepoint hangings, tapestries, and decorative paintings, many of them recent acquisitions, took their place on the walls in the new decorative arts galleries. The Morgan Alcove (fig. 11) and the storefront, however, were dismantled for reinstallation in the new galleries, where the Neoclassical facade of the latter was placed opposite the Bordeaux and Crillon rooms, its vitrines initially used to display a selection of fans.

A windfall of Sèvres porcelain and Sèvres-mounted furniture arrived at the Museum in 1958 as a gift of the

Fig. 9. The Crillon Room in 1954.

Fig. 10. Boudoir from the Hôtel de Crillon, Paris, installed on the third floor of the Bliss residence in New York City. Undated photograph. Courtesy of the Susan Dwight Bliss Collection, George J. Mitchell Department of Special Collections & Archives, Bowdoin College Library, Brunswick, Maine.

Fig. 11. The Morgan Alcove in 1962.

Kress Foundation. This cultural foundation had been established in 1929 by the entrepreneur Samuel H. Kress (1863–1955), who was not only the founder of a highly successful chain of stores but also a noted art collector and philanthropist. A selection of objects from this unprecedented gift—many with stellar provenances that included royal mistresses as well as Louis XV and Marie-Antoinette—was shown in the Museum's Great Hall.[24] Several years later, the Morgan shopfront, with its Neoclassical pilasters and garlands, was moved to a different location within the decorative arts galleries. With Sèvres porcelain vases placed in its windows and the porcelain-mounted furniture from the Samuel H. Kress Collection beyond its opened doors, this new installation offered the visitor the possibility of entering the eighteenth-century boutique of a *marchand-mercier*, or luxury dealer (fig. 12). In May 1960 Rita Reif of the *New York Times* described it as "one of the most intriguing shops ever to open on Fifth Avenue . . . open for browsing, not buying."[25]

Fig. 12. Shopfront from the Île Saint-Louis, Paris, in 1962.

THE INVOLVEMENT OF MR. AND MRS. CHARLES WRIGHTSMAN

With the generous support of Charles B. Wrightsman (1895–1986) and his wife, Jayne, an era of tremendous activity began in the 1960s and continued through the next four decades. The work undertaken during this period not only brought decorative improvements to the existing galleries, such as the creation of new window treatments, for instance, but also, more significantly, saw the acquisition and installation of additional rooms.[26] It was first with the assistance of the acclaimed decorator Stéphane Boudin (1888–1967), president of the firm of Jansen in Paris and a close friend of Mrs. Wrightsman's, that the Museum formulated plans for these expansions and changes. Under the direction of James Parker, a room with paneling from the Hôtel de Varengeville in Paris and another from the Palais Paar in Vienna were created (figs. 13, 14). When they were opened to the public, in November 1969, Parker observed that "the painstaking effort of rehabilitating the scattered pieces of the Varengeville room to form the harmonious interior now at the Museum began early in 1966, when the wooden

Fig. 13. The Varengeville Room in 1968.

shell of the room was erected on a metal framework."[27] The *boiserie*, dating to about 1736–52, was arbitrarily arranged, since it was impossible to reconfigure the original layout. Having been transferred about 1886 from its original location on the boulevard Saint-Germain to a newly built mansion also in Paris, the Hôtel Pillet-Will, on the rue du faubourg Saint-Honoré, the Varengeville paneling was assembled at the Museum to serve as an effective setting for furniture. For this reason the room was enlarged with nine new panels made by the Jansen workshops in Paris to supplement the existing elements.

Fig. 14. The Paar Room in 1969.

The *boiserie* of the adjacent Paar Room, dating to about 1765–72, illustrates well how the influence of French styles spread all over Europe during the eighteenth century (see fig. 14). The paneling, actually the combined woodwork of several rooms at the Palais Paar in Vienna, had subsequently been used in the dining room and antechamber of the London residence of the British politician and art collector Sir Philip Sassoon (1888–1939). At the Museum it was adapted to form the wall decoration of a single large room of approximately the same dimensions as the neighboring Varengeville Room. Mrs. Wrightsman's correspondence with Stéphane Boudin documents the great personal interest and involvement of the donors in all the work that took place. With her customary charm and wit, she wrote in 1966: "The Palais Paar Room will be a dream once we get the windows finished and the curtains up. Useless to say, you and I forgot to order the hardware for the windows (we always manage to forget one thing!). . . . I hated the chimney we chose—too small and too shallow to hold even a candlestick. We must have been drinking daiquiris the day we chose that. Happily the museum possessed a very beautiful one in the same marble but somewhat larger, so for once luck was on our side."[28]

Both rooms were furnished largely with important loans from the Wrightsmans' collection. Rather than re-creations of actual historic rooms, these Wrightsman galleries were considered to be artistic period rooms, aiming "to exhibit in a tasteful manner outstanding examples of the interior architecture and decorative arts of a period."[29] During the summer of 1966, plans were set in motion to remodel the gallery adjoining the Paar and Varengeville rooms, which was completed at the same time. The ceiling raised and its proportions improved, this gallery, known as the Louis XVI Gallery, was embellished with architectural detailing (fig. 15). A beautiful marble and gilt-bronze mantelpiece became the focus of the east wall. In an undated letter to James Parker, Mrs. Wrightsman wrote: "I enclose a photo of a mantel that will be coming your way. Charles bought it

Fig. 15. The Louis XVI Gallery in 1969.

for the long gallery and I hope that you and Jack [John Goldsmith Philips, chairman of the Renaissance and Modern Department] approve. . . . It is the same model as the one at Fontainebleau only prettier I think."[30] The walls of the gallery were decorated with canvases painted in 1777 by Hubert Robert (1733–1808) for the bathroom of the younger brother of Louis XVI, Charles-Philippe, comte d'Artois, at Bagatelle, as well as with Beauvais tapestries after designs by François Boucher (1703–1770). It was further furnished with a pair of rock-crystal and gilt-bronze chandeliers and several pieces of royal furniture (nos. 72, 45), all lent by the Wrightsmans.

The involvement of the donors certainly did not end there, and the renovation of one of the existing rooms was addressed next. Charles Wrightsman wrote in March 1970 that he had "employed Alavoine for the Museum to see if we can straighten out the horrible De Tessé Room and also the room with the pink walls where the Kress furniture is located. These are two horrors and must be reworked."[31] Following Boudin's death in 1967, it was Harold Eberhard Jr., formerly a designer at Jansen's New York office, who continued the work, in collaboration with the decorator Henri Samuel (d. 1996). Samuel had worked as an assistant to Boudin at Jansen at the start of his career but later joined other firms, such as Ramsay and Alavoine, before starting out on his own. The *boiserie* from the Hôtel de Tessé, which had been installed in the area where the Jack and Belle Linsky Galleries are today, was dismantled in 1970 and shipped to France, where additional panels were made for it, so that the room could be enlarged to increase its capacity for the exhibition of furniture and decorative arts. The paneling was repainted a gray-green color.[32] The renovated room was reinstalled in its present location, occupying the remodeled space of two smaller galleries. Various notes written by Mrs. Wrightsman to James Parker indicate that she and her husband were fully engaged in the details of furnishing the room. "We decided to put the sofa and chairs back in the [Tessé] room with the material that is presently on them and only decide after the room is open what material we want. I believe we all agreed to put the two Vanderbilt pieces of furniture in the room."[33] When the grand salon from the Hôtel de Tessé was reopened in November 1972,

Fig. 16. The Tessé Room in 1972.

some of the Museum's most splendid Louis XVI furniture was placed there (fig. 16). The room harbored several pieces made for Marie-Antoinette, including a black lacquer commode and secretary by Jean-Henri Riesener, the bequest of William K. Vanderbilt (nos. 39, 40).[34]

The Wrightsmans continued to refine and add to the galleries that were appropriately named for them. In November 1973, after a period of six months during which they had been closed for improvements in lighting, an additional period room, a paneled salon from the Hôtel de Cabris in Grasse, was opened to the public as well (fig. 17). Before this *boiserie*, dating to about 1774, "landed at the Metropolitan" it had, according to Rita Reif in the *New York Times*, "framed some pretty spectacular dinners down the road" at the Fifth Avenue apartment of Mr. and Mrs. Charles Wrightsman.[35] Eight undecorated narrow panels had been added to this architectural setting, which originally covered the walls of a smaller room, in order to provide more display space for furniture.

In 1976–77 the galleries were remodeled and enlarged under the continued direction of Henri Samuel. He introduced more subtle lighting and oversaw several alterations in the layout of the galleries and the creation of a new period room, with paneling from the Hôtel de Lauzun.[36] At this time the Wrightsman Galleries assumed their current floor plan, with the exception of the Louis XIV–style bedchamber and adjoining gallery,

Fig. 17. The Cabris Room in 1974.

Fig. 18. The Lauzun (Sèvres) Room in 1977.

which were added a decade later. The press release written for the reopening on May 21, 1977, mentioned the substantial number of gifts that were made by Mr. and Mrs. Wrightsman from their incomparable collection of French eighteenth-century decorative arts. The increased exhibition space offered the Museum for the first time the opportunity "to display, in context, the generosity—and dimensions—of the Wrightsmans' contribution." Although a number of their gifts had already been on loan to the Museum, others were shown for the first time, and the incorporation of all these superb pieces from the Wrightsman collection was to bring "the holdings of the Metropolitan Museum to the forefront of the world's collections of French eighteenth-century decorative art."[37]

Also in 1976–77 the shopfront was moved back to its 1954 location, opposite the Bordeaux and Crillon rooms. The woodwork of the Morgan Alcove was transferred to a different place in the galleries, its paneling now supplemented by three large doorframes, making its installation substantially larger than before. Renamed the Louis XV Room, it was flanked by a small space with vitrines for the display of Sèvres porcelain. This narrow gallery also offered visual access to the newly created period room. That interior, installed in the space where the Kress furniture had been shown, consisted of a Neoclassical *boiserie* acquired in 1976 with funds given by the Wrightsmans. The paneling, from an unidentified

eighteenth-century house, had been purchased during the third quarter of the nineteenth century by Baron Jérôme-Frédéric Pichon (1812–1896). A well-known Parisian bibliophile and collector, Pichon reused the *boiserie* for his library at the Hôtel de Lauzun, on the Île Saint-Louis, Paris. Having been stripped of its original paint layers during the nineteenth century, the woodwork—nine principal panels and a modern one—was repainted in France for the Museum; its polychrome palette was inspired by the colors seen in watercolor drawings by Pierre Ranson (1736–1786). Mrs. Wrightsman commented on this work: "While in Paris we went out to see the Lauzun *boiserie*. It is perfectly enchanting and the colors will be marvelous with the Sèvres furniture."[38] Indeed, this paneling became the new setting for the Metropolitan's unique collection of furniture mounted with Sèvres porcelain plaques and decorative wares made by the same manufactory. Not surprisingly, it also became known as the Sèvres Room (fig. 18).

The final expansion of the Wrightsman Galleries took place in 1987. The addition consisted of a late seventeenth-century state bedroom in the style of Louis XIV and an adjoining gallery for the display of additional artworks dating to the reign of the Sun King. It added an earlier dimension to the existing rooms devoted to decorative arts of the eighteenth century. Coordinated and supervised by Harold Eberhard Jr., the new installation was based on designs by Henri Samuel. The bedchamber does not include period paneling; it has an imposing seventeenth-century limestone chimneypiece (no. 73), and its modern architectural features are based on elements in the Hôtel Salé, now the Musée National Picasso, in Paris (fig. 19). The installation was conceived around four rare surviving needlework hangings that had been in the Museum's collection since 1946 (nos. 81–84). Commissioned about 1684–85 by Madame de Montespan, mistress of Louis XIV, these embroideries cover the walls of a bed alcove, which is separated from the rest of the space by a gilded balustrade. A pair of carved oak balusters from the Hoentschel collection served as the model for this balustrade. With crimson cut velvet lining the walls, the room forms an opulent setting for furniture and decorative arts of the Baroque era, several pieces of which have a direct association with Louis XIV. Specially bought for display in this new gallery, for instance, is the small desk, or *bureau brisé*, by the French royal cabinetmaker Alexandre-Jean Oppenordt (1639–1715). It was commissioned for the king's study at the Château de Versailles in 1685 and is one of the few extant pieces of furniture made for the Sun King (no. 12).

THE RENOVATIONS OF 2006–7

The Wrightsman Galleries have long set the standard for period-room display. In his book *Moving Rooms: The Trade in Architectural Salvages*, John Harris described them as being at "the highest artistic level."[39] However, even the best of museum displays needs a face-lift now and then. This became clear during the installation of "Dangerous Liaisons: Fashion and Furniture in the Eighteenth Century" in 2004 (fig. 20). Jointly organized by The Costume Institute and the Department of European Sculpture and Decorative Arts, this exposition was staged in the Wrightsman Galleries. As Patrick Kinmonth, the London-based expert on opera and theater design who was the creative consultant for this show, poetically described it: "When the exhibition closed and after the impossibly fragile dresses, plumes and silks were laid back to rest in their dark, tissue-lined

Fig. 19. The Louis XIV Bedroom in 1987.

drawers . . . the rooms had the sadness of a château when the revellers had left for Paris and the nymphs had departed. . . . Mrs. Charles Wrightsman our 'patronne' was determined that the party should not be over . . . indeed that the old château that had been quietly fading over the decades . . . should be prepared for a new century."[40]

The driving force behind these latest changes was a desire to improve the lighting conditions. The old-fashioned up-lights dating to the 1960s and 1970s could be made more subtle using techniques invented during the revolution that had recently taken place in the field of lighting. Furthermore, fire-prevention and security systems needed to be updated and the airflow to the galleries increased for the well-being and safety of the collections and the public. These considerations led to a rethinking of the presentation of the artworks. In collaboration with Patrick Kinmonth, Museum curators developed a plan for renovating the rooms, which was generously underwritten by Mrs. Wrightsman. Larry French, principal designer of Auerbach Glasow French, an architectural lighting-design firm in San Francisco, led the design campaign, which included the addition of fixtures in the ceilings of the larger period rooms. Incorporating the latest advances in technology, a dimmable system was chosen to direct light on the furniture and artworks. It was decided not to repeat the monotone

Fig. 20. Mannequins dressed in late eighteenth-century *robes à la française* in the Varengeville Room during the "Dangerous Liaisons" exhibition of 2004.

conditions of the past but to vary the light effects in the different spaces by suggesting different times of day and even weather conditions. In some rooms, twilight or evening are simulated and in others the sense of bright daylight or dawn is implied. To this end it was important to use the windows effectively. The backdrops behind the French doors were painted, altering both the quality and the color of the light. All the windows were reglazed with hand-blown glass in order to get the special effect of light pouring in through slightly imperfect panes. Generally the light levels are lower than before to evoke the dimly lit interiors of the past and to create a historical atmosphere for the visitor. The chandeliers and sconces in the nighttime rooms are illuminated, while those in the daylight rooms are not. The wax candles with their flame-shaped, slightly flickering bulbs simulate candle-light as closely as possible. An idea originating with the "Dangerous Liaisons" exhibition was further developed: small fiber-optic lights were incorporated in the uprights of the new barriers. Placed low, these small light sources are an ideal way to highlight the beauty of a gilt-bronze mount or subtly emphasize the carving of a cabriole leg.

When the Wrightsman Galleries were closed in June 2006, all the movable artworks, many of which had been on public view for decades, were put into temporary storage. Curators, conservators, and several outside experts took advantage of the unique opportunity to examine and assess their condition and to address the most urgent conservation issues. In addition to the treatment of a large quantity of gilded seat furniture, all the *boiseries* were carefully cleaned in situ, and, where necessary, areas of surface paint and gilding were consolidated. Pigment analysis was done in all the rooms in an attempt to identify the original paint layer and thus pinpoint the color of the paneling. Careful examination and conservation treatment led to some new attributions. During the cleaning and rewiring of the various light fixtures, for instance, it was discovered that the steel and rock-crystal chandelier in the Paar Room, long thought to be French, is actually Italian (fig. 21). As such, it is one of the few non-French artworks on display in the Wrightsman Galleries; the piece is now attributed to the eighteenth-century Milanese artist Giovanni Battista

Fig. 21. Giovanni Battista Metellino (attributed), twelve-light chandelier, first quarter of the eighteenth century. Steel (gilding not original) and rock crystal, h. 58 in. (147.3 cm). Gift of Mr. and Mrs. Charles Wrightsman, 1977 (1977.1.5).

Fig. 22. The Louis XIV Bedroom.

Metellino (d. 1724), based on similarities with a drawing from his workshop.[41] Milan was one of the most important centers in Europe for the carving of the transparent and colorless quartz known as rock crystal.

Once all the wires and new fixtures had been put in place, smoke detectors, sniffers, sprinkler heads, security cameras, and exit signs were installed and the ceilings were repainted. Although they had been white before, now slightly darker tones, harmonizing with the colors of the walls, were chosen in order to make the boundary recede and to guide the eye of the visitor down to the works of art below. In certain instances, a more dramatic gray was selected, as in the Louis XIV–style bedchamber. Here, the purpose was to imitate the dark hues of the painted ceilings in French Baroque palaces.

The Louis XIV bedchamber was one of several rooms that were substantially altered in their presentation (fig. 22). By removing an old barrier that ran across the space from doorway to doorway, public access has been increased. This change offers the public the chance to walk up to the balustrade surrounding the bed alcove, just as a visitor in the past would have been allowed to do in the state bedroom at Versailles, and have a close look at the embroidered wall- and bed hangings. Opening up the room meant that the furniture hitherto scattered around the floor had to be placed on platforms along the walls for safety's sake and also that the Savonnerie carpet had to be sent to storage.

The contents of all the period rooms were carefully edited in an attempt to gain greater clarity and coherence. Since the Museum does not own any of the furniture or furnishings that originally filled the rooms, the pieces on display were selected for their appropriate scale and function. According to eighteenth-century practice, larger, more formal chairs—so-called *fauteuils meublants*—were arranged around the walls of the rooms used for the reception of official visitors, such as the Varengeville, Tessé, Cabris, and Paar *salons de compagnie* (figs. 23–26). This was also done in the Lauzun Room, which was changed from a salon to a state bedroom, where the daily ritual of the public toilette would have taken place (fig. 32). By contrast, more intimate and private spaces, such as the Bordeaux and Crillon rooms, were filled with furniture on a smaller scale, suitable for the informal

Fig. 23. The Varengeville Room.

Fig. 24. The Tessé Room.

Fig. 25. The Cabris Room.

Fig. 26. The Paar Room.

Fig. 27. The Bordeaux Room.

entertaining of guests without the presence of servants (figs. 27, 28). Given the strength of the Museum's holdings in objects with a royal provenance, the period rooms are, in all likelihood, furnished more grandly than they originally would have been: their paneling derived, after all, from the town houses of the aristocracy and not from Versailles or from any of the other French palaces.

An additional change that took place during the recent renovations was the removal of most paintings from the *boiseries*, where they generally would not have been placed unless they were set into the paneling—the carved woodwork being the main decoration of the walls. One exception is the large self-portrait by Rose-Adélaïde Ducreux (1761–1802), which hangs in the Tessé Room (no. 92). This and other full-length portraits in the galleries bring an eighteenth-century human presence to the rooms and offer at the same time a sense of contemporary fashion in dress. Specifically, the 1783 inventory description of this room, the so-called Salle du Dais at the Hôtel de Tessé, actually listed several family portraits among the furnishings.[42]

Another refinement consisted in moving (where possible) the sconces, which usually framed the overmantel, closer to the mirror, so that the inner arm

Fig. 28. The Crillon Room.

with its candle would be reflected in the glass, as was customary during the eighteenth century. All the curtains were replaced during the 2006–7 renovations, with the exception of the crimson silk taffeta hangings trimmed with gold galloon in the Louis XIV–style bedchamber, which were retained. A 1782 inventory of the Hôtel de Crillon described the curtains in the boudoir as being made of blue gros de Tours, a ribbed silk, of two and one-half widths each and trimmed with fringes and tassels, offering valuable information for the creation of the new draperies.[43] Since it is not known what kinds of curtains the other rooms originally had, authentic styles and fabrics were selected based on pictorial sources and on descriptions culled from contemporary documents. A Neoclassical drawing in the collection of the Cooper-Hewitt, National Design Museum, New York, for instance, served as a model for the Cabris Room curtains (figs. 29, 30). During the eighteenth century there would usually have been unity in the color, material, and trim used for upholstery and window treatments in a particular room. At the Museum, however, it was not possible to follow this practice, because the pieces of seat furniture in the collection are from different sources, and their show covers, some original but mostly later replacements, are not matching. For that reason, and also to make the modern curtains less obtrusive, a different solution was chosen. Cut to the narrow eighteenth-century width and sewn by hand, plain silk taffetas that would best blend with the color of the wall paneling were selected for each of the spaces. Wherever they would be visible, as in the Crillon Room, for instance, copies of eighteenth-century wrought-iron and gilded curtain rods and tieback hooks were used. In the Louis XVI Gallery, one of the door curtains, or *portières*, which were very common at the time, has been draped over the arm of a nearby chair. This somewhat nonchalant placement was inspired by the custom illustrated in eighteenth-century prints and paintings of picking up the rather lengthy curtains and arranging the ends over a screen or on top of a table (fig. 31) .

The Lauzun, or Sèvres, Room underwent the most drastic transformation of all the rooms (fig. 32). Since no eighteenth-century *salon de compagnie* would have been furnished with so many pieces of porcelain-mounted

Fig. 29. *Design for a Window Hanging*, late eighteenth century. Pen and black ink, brush and watercolor, and graphite. Cooper-Hewitt, National Design Museum, Smithsonian Institution, Purchased for the Museum by the Advisory Council, 1908-26-137.

Fig. 30. Window treatment in the Cabris Room.

Fig. 31. Nicolas de Launay, after Nicolas Lafrensen, *The Billet Doux*, 1778. Etching and engraving. The Metropolitan Museum of Art, New York, Harris Brisbane Dick Fund, 1954 (54.533.19).

Fig. 32. The Lauzun Room.

furniture, the space was changed into a formal bedroom. When microscopic paint analysis did not furnish enough information about the original color of the *boiserie*, the woodwork was repainted in a gray-green tone to harmonize with the three grisaille overdoor paintings. A glue-based, quick-drying paint known as distemper, mixed according to traditional recipes, was used, and late eighteenth-century pieces of furniture and decorative objects, mostly from storage, were selected for display. A magnificent *lit à la duchesse en impériale* (bed with a domed flying tester) by Georges Jacob now occupies a place of honor (no. 38). It received major conservation treatment to clean and consolidate its delicately carved and gilded woodwork, and the fragile and incomplete Beauvais tapestry bed hangings were replaced with modern silk damask. Several new mattresses were ordered to bring the bedding back to its eighteenth-century height and restore its boxlike appearance.

The two wall cases in the narrow gallery just outside the Lauzun Room were refitted for the exhibition of French silver, largely drawn from the incomparable bequest made by Catherine D. Wentworth in 1948. Forming a welcome pendant to the display in the Morgan shopfront windows nearby, many more objects are now shown than before, including some rare surviving pieces of early eighteenth-century table silver.

Displaced from the Lauzun Room, the Museum's outstanding collection of porcelain-mounted furniture and Sèvres decorative wares needed a new setting. They became the focus of a separate gallery (fig. 33), once used as a smoking lounge, that runs between the Louis XIV–style bedchamber and the Tessé Room. Its walls painted a strong turquoise blue inspired by the Sèvres ground color known as *bleu céleste* (sky blue), this gallery offers a dazzling array of *bonheurs-du-jour* (small desks), jewelry caskets, and secretaries placed on platforms.

In the four wall cases, part of a dessert service (no. 103) that belonged to Louis-René-Édouard, prince de Rohan-Guémenée (1734–1803), and ornamental vases and potpourri vessels are exhibited. This new display allows visitors to examine the porcelain pieces close up and truly appreciate the superb quality of the flower painting and gilding. A C-shaped display case was installed in the small vestibule between the French Renaissance Gallery and the new Sèvres Gallery. Using the space formerly occupied by a freight elevator, this shallow vitrine holds a wealth of gold snuffboxes and *étuis* (cases) as well as several fans; none of these precious objects had been shown for many years.

There has been considerable discussion about the merits of period rooms during the past several decades. In his *New York Times* review following the most recent renovation of the Wrightsman Galleries, Ken Johnson referred to them as "part time machine, part 'Masterpiece Theater' . . . a paradoxical museum animal."[44] They are often criticized as being inaccurate or completely fabricated and detrimental to the study of individual works of art.

A number of museums, both in Europe and in America, have dismantled their rooms, usually because of questions of quality and authenticity of the paneling and lack of appropriate furnishings. The removal of such paneled rooms certainly allows for more flexibility in the display of decorative arts. The Metropolitan Museum, however, remains strongly committed to its French period rooms, which evoke rather than reconstitute actual interiors. However artificial these rooms may be in certain aspects—with paneling from one source and floors, mantelpieces, furniture, and objects from others, and with modern ceilings, new fabrics, simulated daylight, sprinklers, and fiber-optic lights—they are, nevertheless, the favorite destination for many of our visitors. Despite all these contradictions, the elegant French rooms at the Museum are beautiful settings that allow the furniture and decorative arts displayed inside to be seen in a proper context and thus to regain their scale and purpose. More important, in this increasingly visual age the Wrightsman Galleries offer the visitor an opportunity to be seduced and delighted as well as a chance to recapture the past.

Fig. 33. The Sèvres Gallery.

1. John Adams to Abigail Adams, April 12, 1778, in J. Adams and A. Adams 1774–83/1970, p. 329.
2. Robinson 1910, p. 5.
3. Robinson 1907, p. 98.
4. C. Purdon Clarke, Director of the Metropolitan Museum, to J. Pierpont Morgan, February 8, 1908, The Morgan Library and Museum, New York.
5. Robinson 1907, p. 98.
6. Ibid.
7. Robinson 1910, p. 5.
8. For a full description of the Wing of Decorative Arts, see Robinson et al. 1910.
9. "New Wing of the Metropolitan Museum" 1910.
10. Gary A. Reynolds in *Walter Gay* 1980, p. 75, no. 51.
11. Breck and Rogers 1925, pp. xix–xxi.
12. Joseph Breck to J. Pierpont Morgan Jr., Paris, February 29, 1920, The Morgan Library and Museum, New York.
13. Rogers 1921, p. 72.
14. Ibid.
15. J. Pierpont Morgan Jr. to Edward Robinson, March 3, 1920, The Morgan Library and Museum, New York.
16. Rogers 1921.
17. Meyric R. Rogers in Breck and Rogers 1925, p. 290.
18. Ibid., p. 292.
19. This is in contrast to a so-called historic period room, which presents an interior as it once existed with most of its original furnishings. See Alexander 1964.
20. Rogers and Breck 1923, p. 267.
21. Deaccessioned in 1953 and sold to the Los Angeles County Museum of Art; acquired by the M. H. De Young Memorial Museum, San Francisco, about 1966; sold by the Fine Arts Museums of San Francisco through the auction house Butterfield and Butterfield, San Francisco, June 18, 1997, lot 4072. The salon was acquired by the Musée des Beaux-Arts, Dijon. The bedroom was sold again at Christie's, New York, April 20, 2007, lot 147.
22. Remington 1954, p. 68.
23. Pons 1995, p. 106.
24. Knox 1958.
25. Reif 1960.
26. The 1962 proposals by Jansen, Paris, for new window treatments for the Crillon and Bordeaux rooms are included in Abbott 2006, p. 195.
27. Parker 1969, p. 136.
28. Quoted in Abbott 2006, p. 190.
29. Parker 1969, pp. 144–45.
30. Jayne Wrightsman to James Parker, undated letter, archives of the Department of European Sculpture and Decorative Arts (hereafter ESDA Archives).
31. Charles B. Wrightsman to Joseph V. Noble, Vice Director of Operations at the Metropolitan Museum, March 2, 1970, ESDA Archives.
32. When the room was first exhibited, its paneling was a solid gray, but it was repainted white in 1956. Parker 1996d, pp. 101–2.
33. Jayne Wrightsman to James Parker, August 25, 1972, ESDA Archives.
34. "Museum Re-opens Magnificent Louis XVI Salon," Metropolitan Museum press release, November 1972.
35. Reif 1973.
36. Parker 1977.
37. "Newly-Refurbished and Enlarged Wrightsman Galleries to Reopen May 21 at Metropolitan Museum," Metropolitan Museum press release, May 1977.
38. Jayne Wrightsman to Olga Raggio, Chairman of the Department of European Sculpture and Decorative Arts, June 15, 1976, ESDA Archives.
39. Harris 2007, p. 6.
40. Quoted from a text prepared (but not given) by Patrick Kinmonth for a symposium held at the Metropolitan Museum on February 15, 2008, entitled "The Past, Present, and Future of the Period Room: A Symposium in Honor of the Reopening of the Wrightsman Galleries for French Decorative Arts."
41. We are grateful to Käthe Klappenbach, Berlin, for this new attribution. For related examples by Metellino, see Klappenbach 2001, pp. 27, 31–32, 65–66, 114–15, figs. 15, 22, 60, 62. The chandelier was published in Watson 1966c, pp. 348–49, no. 178.
42. Pons 1995, pp. 153, 298.
43. Ibid., p. 358.
44. K. Johnson 2007.

The Wrightsman Galleries for French Decorative Arts

The Paris way of living is extremely magnificent.

—Francis Seymour-Conway, Earl of Hertford, to Horace Walpole,
   Earl of Orford, November 11, 1763

Wood Paneling and Furniture

DANIËLLE KISLUK-GROSHEIDE

According to a rigid guild system that had its roots in medieval France, the eighteenth-century French craftsmen working in wood were subdivided into several categories. Trained in different techniques, which encouraged a high level of specialization, the so-called *menuisiers* (joiners) made furniture such as chairs and beds out of solid, mostly native, wood. For their part, the *ébénistes* (cabinetmakers; from the French word for ebony, an exotic wood that was used during the seventeenth century for veneered furniture) excelled in the techniques of veneering and marquetry, often choosing exotic timbers for the embellishment of case pieces. A different group of carpenters, the so-called *menuisiers en bâtiments*, were responsible for the creation of wall paneling, or *lambris*, which would lend the interior an architectural character (see figs. 34, 35). Not surprisingly, it was often an architect who provided the overall plan for the paneling, leaving the carved ornament to a special designer. When the *lambris* was kept low, occupying only about one-fourth or one-fifth of the total height of the room, it was known as the *lambris d'appui* (dado), according to André-Jacob Roubo (1739–1791), author of the informative treatise *L'Art du menuisier*. When the paneling covered the entire wall space between the floor and the cornice, it was known as the *lambris de hauteur*.[1] Although the *menuisier* was allowed to adorn the panels with simple moldings, a decorative carver would be called upon to execute the sculptural elements. The *menuisier* cut and prepared the wood, usually oak, leaving enough thickness for a sculptor to create the additional decoration, the design for which was sometimes sketched in charcoal on the wall. Such a sketch would enable the patron to envision the work in situ before it was completed. That the *boiseries* could add a substantial expense to a construction budget is illustrated by a remark of Élisabeth-Charlotte, duchesse d'Orléans (1652–1722), who wrote in 1708 that the paneling of the new palace at Meudon alone cost the dauphin 110,000 francs.[2]

Most woodwork was painted in light colors—a white ground with highlights in gold being the noblest combination, according to Jacques-François Blondel's architectural treatise of 1771–77, *Cours d'architecture*.[3] It was also the most fashionable, if we are to believe Horace Walpole (1717–1797). The British politician and author observed in 1765 from Paris, "Their houses in town are all white and gold, and looking-glass; I never know one from another" and "I have seen but one idea in all the houses here; the rooms are white and gold, or white."[4]

Popular contemporary manuals such as Jean-Félix Watin's *L'Art de faire et d'employer le vernis*, first published in 1772 and reissued many times under different titles, offered recipes for various types of oil- or glue-based paint. The latter was known as distemper and it lent itself to varnishing, giving the woodwork "a most sumptuous embellishment . . . exhibiting the freshness of porcelain."[5]

Extensive and very successful use was made of mirrors in the French interior, as was frequently commented upon in the diaries of foreign travelers. Samuel Johnson (1709–1784) wrote in 1775, for instance, that the house of Mr. Argenson (possibly Marc-Antoine-René de Voyer de Paulmy, marquis d'Argenson [1722–1787]) "was almost wainscoted with looking glasses, and covered with gold. . . . They always place mirrors [*sic*] to reflect their rooms."[6] Visitors like Dr. Johnson toured the Parisian workshops where the glass, having been cast in Normandy, was polished and silvered.[7] They marveled at the size and perfection of the work, which was considered to be far superior to that created in England. Still a luxurious and expensive commodity, large sheets of mirror glass helped to reflect and multiply the limited

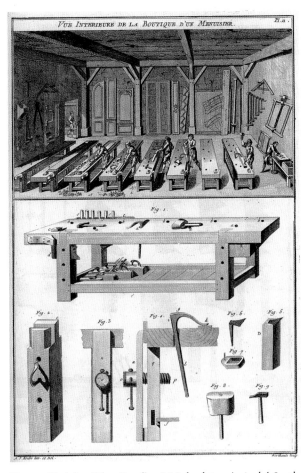

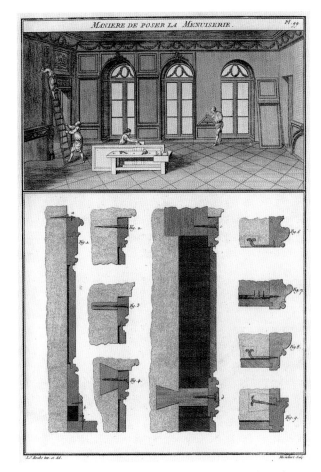

Fig. 34. *Workshop Where Paneling Is Made*, plate 11 in André-Jacob Roubo, *L'Art du menuisier*, vol. 1, pt. 1 (Paris, 1769). The Metropolitan Museum of Art, New York, The Thomas J. Watson Library.

Fig. 35. *Paneling Being Installed*, plate 99 in André-Jacob Roubo, *L'Art du menuisier*, vol. 1, pt. 2 (Paris, 1770). The Metropolitan Museum of Art, New York, The Thomas J. Watson Library.

amount of light in the eighteenth-century interior. In addition, they offered interesting perspective views both from inside the building and from outside. Hester (Mrs. Henry) Thrale (1741–1821), a friend and traveling companion of Dr. Johnson's, remarked in her journal for October 14, 1775, that the tent-shaped bed of Mr. "D'Argençon" was "repeated eight Times by Mirrors placed accordingly."[8] English businessman Thomas Bentley (1731–1780), having made a social call on Mr. Godfrey in Paris in 1776, commented on the three large looking glasses at the far end of one of his rooms. Through these mirrors Godfrey enjoyed "the prospect of the Louvre, the hotels [mansions] and buildings on the contrary side, the River Siene [*sic*], and the plantations in

the Champs Elysées both ways. I fancy there can be no apartments in all Paris so advantageously situated for a city view."[9]

Epigraph on page 23. Walpole 1937–83, vol. 38 (1974), p. 220.

1. Roubo 1769–75, vol. 1, pt. 2 (1770), p. 165.
2. Letter to her aunt Sophia, Duchess of Hanover (1630–1714), September 23, 1708, in Orléans 1672–1722/1970, p. 132.
3. Blondel 1771–77, vol. 5 (1777), p. 75.
4. Horace Walpole to Lady Suffolk, September 20, 1765, and Walpole to Anne Pitt, December 25, 1765, in Walpole 1937–83, vol. 31 (1961), pp. 49, 87.
5. Watin 1778/1975, p. 76.
6. Journal entry for October 14, 1775, in S. Johnson 1775/1932, p. 172.
7. Journal entry for October 23, 1775, ibid., pp. 178–79.
8. Thrale 1775/1932, p. 116.
9. Bentley 1776/1977, p. 36.

Paneling

1. The Louis XV Room

Formerly known as the Morgan Alcove
Paris, ca. 1720–25, with later additions (dado,
cornice, and door surrounds)
Carved, painted, and gilded oak
H. of room 19 ft. (5.79 m), w. 18 ft. 10½ in.
(5.75 m), l. 25 ft. 8½ in. (7.83 m)
Gift of J. Pierpont Morgan, 1907 (07.225.147)

Jean-Félix Watin (b. 1728) stated in the second edition of his manual *L'Art de faire et d'employer le vernis* that "*blanc de Roi* [a white distemper] . . . is the friend of gold; that is to say, it makes the gold sparkle and stand out more because of its beautiful matte surface."[1] This remark still rings true for this early eighteenth-century paneling, even though as many as six applications of paint and gilding have covered its surface. The main decoration consists of trophies of the four seasons suspended from bow-knotted ribbons carved on the rounded corner panels. A sheaf of wheat, farming equipment, a straw hat, and a parasol, among other objects, are emblematic of summer, whereas a basket of flowers, gardening tools, and birds symbolize spring. Autumn is represented by a horn of plenty, a basket of grapes, a hunting rifle, and a horn, while musical instruments, a jester's bauble, theatrical masks, and candles symbolizing indoor activities refer to winter. The four seasons are also alluded to in the masks and festoons above each of these trophies, which in the past have been related to drawings by the designer and sculptor François-Antoine Vassé (1681–1736). More recently, however, they have been compared to work by the talented François Roumier (active 1716–48). Roumier, a decorative carver employed by the Bâtiments du Roi, the agency in charge of the construction and maintenance of the various French royal palaces, was during the 1720s responsible for much of the carved interior decoration at the Château de Versailles. In 1723–25, Roumier designed and carved a series of sixteen panels with trophy decorations for the choir of the Parisian church of the Noviciat des Jacobins, the present church of Saint Thomas d'Aquin. The engraved designs of this work, now dispersed, bear stylistic similarities to the Museum's woodwork. The original location of this early eighteenth-century paneling has not been identified, although it was once thought to have come from the Château de Marly. The *boiserie* was sold several times during the nineteenth century and belonged at one point to the French history painter Joseph-Désiré Court (1797–1865), who reportedly had acquired them from a Parisian cabinetmaker and dealer in antique furniture and woodwork called Monbro, probably Georges-Alphonse-Bonifacio (1807–1884). Court's effects were auctioned off in 1866 following his death. At that point the paneling still included six over-door panels instead of the Museum's single pair, carved with trophies of music, now placed above the two side mirrors, indicating that the *boiserie* was originally made for a larger room.

1. Watin 1778/1975, p. 84.

References: Pératé and Brière 1908, vol. 2, pp. 26–27, pls. XLIII–XLVII; Parker 1977, pp. 377–380, pl. V, fig. 1; Pons 1986, p. 168, pls. 468, 469, 471–74 (engravings of trophies for the church of the Noviciat des Jacobins).

2. The Varengeville Room

Paris, ca. 1736–52 (with later additions)
Carved, painted, and gilded oak
H. of room 18 ft. 3¾ in. (5.58 m), w. 23 ft. 2½ in.
(7.07 m), l. 40 ft. 6½ in. (12.36 m)
Purchase, Mr. and Mrs. Charles Wrightsman
Gift, 1963 (63.228.1)

Superb carving, partly in high relief, constitutes the chief glory of this paneling, which comes from one of the private residences of eighteenth-century Paris, the Hôtel de Varengeville, which still stands, much altered, at 217, boulevard Saint-Germain. It was built by the architect Jacques Gabriel (1667–after 1742) for Charlotte-Angélique Courtin, comtesse de Varengeville, whose daughter, Jeanne-Angélique Roque de Varengeville, duchesse de Villars, inherited the house in 1732. The duchesse de Villars sold the house four years later to Marie-Marguerite d'Allègre, comtesse de Ruppelmonde, who owned the building until her death in 1752 and who is likely to have commissioned the Museum's paneling. Certain aspects of the carved ornament, such as the placement of the long-necked birds perched on the scrolling frames of the wall panels and mirrors, are related to a drawing that has been attributed to Nicolas Pineau (1648–1754). Pineau is primarily known for his highly asymmetrical and deliciously whimsical designs in the high Rococo style. That full-blown phase of the Rococo is not yet attained in the delicate and spirited decoration of the Varengeville paneling, which is still largely symmetrical. Although the *boiserie* is richly embellished with C-scrolls, S-scrolls, palmettes, sprigs of flowers, coiling vines, and rocaille motifs, most of the attention is lavished on a series of trophies (eleven of which are original; the remainder are copies made for installation in the Museum). In addition to representations of the four seasons, the other trophies allude to concepts and qualities ranging from military fame and princely glory, to truthfulness, commerce, gardening, music, and poetry. The paneling was transferred to a newly built residence at 31, rue du faubourg Saint-Honoré, Paris, in the late nineteenth century by comte Frédéric-Alexis-Louis Pillet-Will, from where it was sold in 1963.

References: Parker 1969, pp. 129–39, figs. 6, 7, 9–14; James Parker in Watson and Dauterman 1970, pp. 12–21, no. 292, ill.; Parker 1996e, ill.

3. The Paar Room

Vienna, ca. 1765–72 (with later additions)
Designed by Isidor Canevale (1730–1786);
made by Johann Georg Leithner (1725–1785)
and his assistants
Carved, painted, and gilded pine
H. of room 16 ft. (4.87 m), w. 24 ft. 6½ in.
(7.48 m), l. 40 ft. 6 in. (12.34 m)
Purchase, Mr. and Mrs. Charles Wrightsman
Gift, 1963 (63.229.1)

According to the Viennese travel guide *Nützliches Adress und Reisebuch*, published in 1792, "the House of Prince Paar . . . especially deserves to be seen because of the splendor of its interior settings, carried out under the direction of the architect Canevale."[1] Among its glories were the French-style paneled rooms.

Formerly at 30 Wollzeile, not far from Saint Stephen's Cathedral, Palais Paar was built about 1630 for the postmaster of the Holy Roman Empire, Baron Johann Christoph von Paar. During the second half of the eighteenth century the state apartments and living quarters of this stately residence were renovated for one of his descendants, Count Wenzel Johann Joseph von Paar, in a tempered version of the Rococo style. According to contemporary documents, the French-born architect Isidor Canevale was responsible for the paneling designs, which were executed by the sculptor Johann Georg Leithner. Displaying triple moldings that are enriched with foliate and shell motifs, floral ornament, and either C- or S-shaped scrolls, the Museum's paneling comes from various rooms originally at the back of the palace. They were decorated more sparingly than the richly embellished reception rooms behind the main facade. About 1931, before the building was demolished, most of the *boiseries* were dismantled and sold to the Parisian decorating firm of Jansen. The British politician and art collector Sir Philip Sassoon (1888–1939) acquired some of this paneling in 1934 for installation in his London house, at 45 Park Lane. It was, however, bought back by Jansen in the 1950s and later purchased by Mr. and Mrs. Charles Wrightsman for use at the Museum. Microscopic paint analysis has revealed three tones of gray distemper, probably the original paint layers, on different elements of the woodwork, thereby underscoring its composite nature. The current blue-green paint surface was applied by Jansen before the Wrightsmans acquired the room in 1963. This color was then believed to be close to the original shade; cross sections taken during the most recent conservation treatment indicate that the paneling was indeed once painted a light blue. That color, however, is now known to be not the earliest but one of the subsequent layers.

1. *Nützliches Adress und Reisebuch* 1792, pp. 20–21.

References: Parker 1969, pp. 139–44, figs. 22, 25; James Parker in Watson and Dauterman 1970, pp. 22–31, no. 293, ill.; Parker 1996c, ill.; Baumeister et al. 2009, pp. 202–5, figs. 1, 2.

4. The Tessé Room

Paris, ca. 1768–72 (with later additions)
Made by Nicolas Huyot (1700–1791); carved by
Pierre Fixon (active 1748–88) and/or his son
Louis-Pierre Fixon (b. 1748)
Carved, painted, and gilded oak; four plaster
overdoor reliefs
H. of room 16 ft. (4.87 m), w. 29 ft. 6½ in. (9 m),
l. 33 ft. 7½ in. (10.25 m)
Gift of Mrs. Herbert N. Straus, 1942 (42.203.1)

The salon is the assembly room, used for festive occasions. It is here that the greatest formality prevails; in this room, magnificence must unfold; wealth must be lavished; and the Artist must deploy his taste and his genius. Marbles, bronzes, gilding, sculpture, painting, and glasses will come to his aid; tapestries, which we have raised to such a degree of beauty, may enrich the effect. Rock crystal for the lusters, girandoles, and candelabra; precious statues; the richest of vases; the rarest of porcelains; all may combine to improve the room.

—Nicolas Le Camus de Mézières,
Le Génie de l'architecture

Following a disastrous fire, the residence at 1, quai Voltaire, was rebuilt between 1765 and 1768 at the behest of the widowed Marie-Charlotte de Béthune-Charost, comtesse de Tessé (1713–1783), and her son René Mans de Froulay (1736–1814), who had acquired the ruined building on the condition that a new mansion would be constructed. Although contemporary guidebooks credit the designs to the architect Pierre-Noël Rousset (1715–1793), it appears that the architect-contractor Louis Le Tellier (ca. 1700–1785) was primarily responsible for the creation of this Paris house with its dignified facade, still standing today on the left bank of the Seine, near the Pont du Carrousel. Since the accounts were not settled until April of 1772, it is likely that the interior decoration was not completed before then. The Museum's paneling with its refined carving in the Neoclassical style was the work of woodworker Nicolas Huyot, a *maître menuisier* about whom little is known.

The carving was done by the sculptor Pierre Fixon or his son Louis-Pierre, or perhaps the two in collaboration. The Fixons may also have created the plaster overdoor reliefs representative of the four seasons (see detail page 32, left). The marble sculptor Jean-Baptiste-Antoine Le Franc, who like the Fixons had worked with Le Tellier on various other projects, was responsible for the blue turquin marble mantelpiece, which is original to the room.

The paneling acquired by the Museum decorated the largest of the formal reception rooms that were aligned, or laid out *en enfilade*, on the first floor of the building (the American second floor). Particularly beautiful are the coffered triumphal arches executed in perspective that frame the four mirrors and are crowned by laurel branches and floral wreaths (see detail page 32, right). The 1783 inventory drawn up after the death of the comtesse de Tessé indicates that this room was called the Salle du Dais (Canopy Room) after the large tester or canopy that must have been mounted on the wall opposite the windows. Underneath this crimson damask tent, which was enriched with gold embroidered appliqués of the Tessé family coat of arms, the comtesse or her son presumably received their guests. Although not of royal birth, Madame de Tessé was the widow of René Mans de Froulay (1707–1742), comte de Tessé and marquis de Laverdin, as well as a Spanish grandee. In addition to a six-leaf folding chamber screen, the room was furnished with twenty-nine chairs all covered with different crimson fabrics, a small veneered bookcase, and a gilt-bronze cartel clock with movement by Voisin. Several family portraits and two tapestries of landscape scenes were hung on the side walls. The 1783 inventory of the hôtel did not list any curtains in the room; perhaps none were hung, in order not to obscure the lovely view from the three large windows of the Seine and the Louvre and Tuileries palaces across the water.

Epigraph. Le Camus de Mézières 1780/1992, p. 111.

References: Remington 1943, ill.; Parker 1977, pp. 381–83, pls. VI, VII, figs. 3, 6; Pons 1995, pp. 292–300, ill.; Parker 1996d, ill.

5. The Lauzun Room

Paris, ca. 1770 (with one modern panel)
Carved and painted oak
H. of room 16 ft. 3¾ in. (4.97 m), w. 26 ft. 11 in. (8.19 m), l. 26 ft. 11½ in. (8.21 m)
Purchase, Mr. and Mrs. Charles Wrightsman Gift, 1976 (1976.91.1)

The design of this Neoclassical paneling incorporates fluted pilasters crowned with Corinthian capitals and three sets of double doors that alternate with carved panels. The latter are embellished below with symmetrical arabesques and vases in low relief and with graceful swags at the top, but they all differ slightly from each other. No eighteenth-century provenance has been discovered for this woodwork, but by 1874 it had been installed in the first-floor (American second floor) gallery of the Hôtel de Lauzun, a seventeenth-century residence on the Île Saint-Louis in Paris. The house was then occupied by the baron Jérôme-Frédéric Pichon (1812–1896), a well-known collector and bibliophile. Stripped to its bare oak and stained a dark shade of brown, the paneling lined the walls of his library. With its four large windows overlooking the quay and the river Seine, this room was the setting for eccentric parties at which Pichon entertained literary contemporaries such as Charles Baudelaire and Théophile Gautier. The paneling remained in place until the baron's grandson, Louis Pichon, acquired the hôtel in 1905. Having a stricter aesthetic sense and a desire to restore the seventeenth-century appearance of the gallery, he dismantled and sold the *boiserie*. It arrived at the Museum in 1976. When microscopic analysis revealed little

5 (detail)

6. The Cabris Room

Paris, ca. 1774 (with later additions)
Carved, painted, and gilded oak
H. of room 11 ft. 8½ in. (3.56 m), w. 22 ft.
10½ in. (6.96 m), l. 25 ft. 6 in. (7.77 m)
Purchase, Mr. and Mrs. Charles Wrightsman
Gift, 1972 (1972.276.1)

*The splendour of the French nobles is
confined to their town-residence: that
of the English is more usefully
distributed in their country-seats.*
—Edward Gibbon, *Memoirs of My Life*

When installed in the Hôtel de Cabris
in Grasse, this paneling lined the
walls of a considerably smaller space
than it does today. Originally the
room had five sets of double doors
(now reduced to four) and an equal
number of mirrors (now three). A
wonderful harmony must have been
achieved by alternating the carved
and gilded woodwork with the reflec-
tive glass surfaces. Mirrors were very

6 (detail)

about the original paint below the
stain, the woodwork was repainted in
a monochrome gray-green distemper
to harmonize with the three grisaille
overdoors, which have been associated with the paneling but did not
originally belong to it (see detail
above). Showing children representing spring, summer, and winter,
they are duplicates of the overdoors
representing the four seasons painted

about 1787 by Piat Joseph Sauvage
(1744–1818) for Queen Marie-
Antoinette's dairy at Rambouillet.

References: Parker 1977, pp. 383–86, 388,
pl. VIII, fig. 8; Baumeister et al. 2009,
pp. 208–9, figs. 9–11.

effectively used in eighteenth-century French interiors, offering unlimited perspective views and magically making the rooms appear larger than they were. The Museum's paneling was commissioned in Paris for the new residence of Jean-Paul de Clapiers, marquis de Cabris (1749–1813), and his wife, Louise de Mirabeau (1752–1807), which had been built between 1771 and 1774 by the little-

known Milanese architect Giovanni Orello, who resided in Grasse. The Parisian sculptor André Brenet (ca. 1734–after 1792) supervised the interior decoration of the house. According to the inventory drawn up in February 1778, the hôtel had been left unfinished and in a state of disarray and this *boiserie*, intended for the *salon de compagnie*, or reception room, remained unpacked and in

crates. This must have been due to the calamity that befell the family that same year: the marquis de Cabris had been declared insane and his wife confined to a convent. It is probably also the reason that the overdoors and panels over the mirrors were not completed. The paneling was installed later, and it remained in the house until 1910, when it was purchased by E. M. Hodgkins, a dealer from England who resided in Paris. Together with the rest of Hodgkins's effects, the woodwork elements were auctioned off in 1937. Duveen Brothers, the international firm of dealers and decorators, sold the paneling to the Charles Wrightsmans in 1957 for use in the dining room of their Fifth Avenue apartment. It was for this installation that the paneling was first rearranged and augmented.

The decoration of the room, with its dignified moldings, geometrical forms, and preference for Greek and Roman ornament, is a pure expression of the Neoclassical style. The rounded corners are carved with different trophies of musical instruments that are suspended from bow-tied ribbons and hung from an imaginary nail (see detail page 36, below). Smoking incense burners on tripod stands, a motif derived from classical antiquity, embellish the upper door panels, while those below show flaming torches. Both sets of panels have, in addition, crossed laurel and olive branches, ancient symbols of victory and peace. Here they may refer to the local vegetation, just as the incense burners may allude to the perfume industry of the Provence region. The combined use of dulled and burnished gilding creates a particularly lively effect, as is seen, for instance, in the laurel leaves with their beautifully rippled edges that are left matte, contrasting with the lustrous stems of their branches.

Epigraph. Gibbon 1788–93/1966, p. 125.

References: James Parker in Watson and Dauterman 1970, pp. 32–39, no. 294, ill.; Parker 1977, pp. 390, 392, pl. X, fig. 13; Parker 1996a, ill.; Scherf 2008a.

7. Shopfront, Île Saint-Louis

Paris, 1775–77 (with later replacements)
Étienne Séjournant (master in 1772)
Carved oak
H. 13 ft. 1 in. (3.98 m), w. 20 ft. 5¾ in. (7.63 m), d. 1 ft. 1½ in. (34.3 cm)
Gift of J. Pierpont Morgan, 1920 (20.154)

Then as now, eighteenth-century travelers to Paris frequented the various shops of the city, which, in the opinion of some, did not live up to those in London. Particularly disgruntled was the Reverend William Cole (1714–1782), who visited France in the fall of 1765 and penned these words in his journal: "The Shops at Paris are the poorest gloomy Dungeons you can possibly conceive, however rich their Contents may be: as the Brillancy & Shew of ours in London make one of its cheif [*sic*] Beauties & Ornaments, so the dead Gloom of the City of Paris is nothing beholden to its Tradesmen in shewing their Goods to the best Advantage."[1] Cole probably exaggerated the situation, but surly and disagreeable the shopkeepers could indeed be, and furthermore they were known to overcharge their customers, who, in turn, were forced to haggle their prices down.

It is not known what kind of merchandise was originally displayed behind the windows of the Museum's shopfront, formerly located at 3, quai de Bourbon, on the Île Saint-Louis in Paris. Photographs taken about 1900 show that it was then occupied by a grocery store. The building itself and four others adjacent to it had been constructed in the mid-seventeenth century by Pierre Mercier, and all of them housed businesses at street level. During the last quarter of the

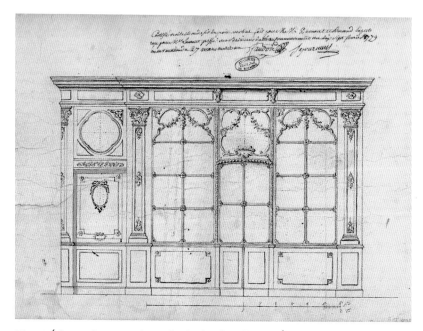

Fig. 36. Étienne Séjournant, design for the shopfront from the Île Saint-Louis, Paris, 1775–77. Archives Nationales, Paris (AN zlj 1045).

eighteenth century, the little-known *menuisier* Étienne Séjournant was employed by the owner of two of the buildings to create a new oak storefront for one of them. Séjournant's drawing (fig. 36) shows some lingering Rococo details, but they were altered in the executed work, which has a purely Neoclassical design, featuring pilasters crowned by Corinthian capitals and symmetrical floral swags. The oak facade was originally painted, but having been exposed to the elements, the woodwork has suffered much over time. César Daly included a measured drawing of the shopfront in his *Motifs historiques d'architecture et de sculpture d'ornement* of 1870, and it already shows some modifications. The original doors of this rare surviving storefront were missing and much of its carved decoration was lost when the Parisian dealer and decorating firm of Carlhian acquired the facade in 1917.

1. Cole 1765/1931, p. 50.

References: Daly 1870, vol. 2, pl. 23; Parker 1977, pp. 388, 390, pl. ix, figs. 9, 10; Courtin 1997, ill.

8. The Crillon Room

Paris, 1777–80
Designed by Pierre-Adrien Pâris (1747–1819)
Painted and gilded oak
H. of room 9 ft. 3½ in. (2.83 m), w. 15 ft. 5½ in.
(4.71 m), l. 14 ft. 3½ in. (4.36 m)
Gift of Susan Dwight Bliss, 1944 (44.128)

*[Arabesques] are an inexhaustible
source of ways to decorate in a
beautiful style the interior and exterior
of modern buildings, furniture, and
even clothes.*

—Charles-Louis Clérisseau, 1779

Delightful arabesques painted in pastel colors on a soft blue ground form the chief decoration of this paneling, which once lined the walls of a boudoir located next to the bedroom of Louis-Marie-Augustin, fifth duc d'Aumont (1709–1782), one of the four First Gentlemen of the King's Bedchamber. In 1776 he rented an unfinished town house that had been constructed for the builder and entrepreneur Louis-François Trouard (1729–1794). It was one of several private mansions erected behind a facade built in a grand Neoclassical style by Jacques-Ange Gabriel (1698–1782) on the place Louis XV, now the place de la Concorde. A man of taste as well as a significant art collector, the duc d'Aumont engaged the architect Pierre-Adrien Pâris to design the interior decoration for his new abode. Having studied in Rome, partly at the duke's expense, Pâris would have been familiar with the early sixteenth-century decorative wall paintings executed by Raphael and his assistants in the Vatican loggias. Raphael's work clearly served as inspiration for the embellishment of the Museum's paneling, as it shows similar charming and lighthearted motifs, such as small animals balancing on garlands and rolling acanthus scrolls. The exterior windows of this intimate polyhedral boudoir, which was painted by an unknown artist, gave access to a balcony with views toward the rue des Champs-Élysées (now the rue Boissy d'Anglas).

Set into the wall paneling are four mirrors angled to reflect the arabesque decoration. (The mirror inside the niche is a replacement for the

original pane of clear glass that allowed light to shine into the stairwell behind the room.) According to the 1782 inventory drawn up after the duke's death, the boudoir was furnished with four stools, two armchairs, and an *ottomane*, or comfortable sofa, described as having three backs. Each stool was most likely placed under one of the mirrors, and the *ottomane*, complete with cushions, pillows, and

bolsters, must have stood inside the niche. All the seat furniture was upholstered in blue moiré silk, the same color as that of the gros de Tours (ribbed silk) curtains. Although most of the furnishings and collections of the duc d'Aumont were sold at a celebrated auction that took place in the house in 1782, the woodwork of this room stayed in the building. The hôtel was acquired six years later by

François-Félix-Dorothée des Balbes de Berton, comte de Crillon (1748–1820), and it remained the property of his descendants until the early twentieth century.

Epigraph. Quoted in Hautecoeur 1912, p. 46.

References: Parker 1977, pp. 392–93, pl. XI, fig. 16; Pons 1995, pp. 356–59, ill.; Parker 1996b, ill.; Jordan 2008, p. 50.

9. The Bordeaux Room

Bordeaux, ca. 1785 (with later additions)
Attributed to Barthélemy Cabirol
(ca. 1732–1786) and his workshop
Carved and painted pine
H. of room 13 ft. 2½ in. (4 m), max. diam. 18 ft.
1¾ in. (5.53 m)
Gift of Mrs. Herbert N. Straus, 1943 (43.158.1)

Carving over a door lintel

Bordeaux, an important seaport on the Garonne River in southwest France, experienced unprecedented economic and demographic growth during the second half of the eighteenth century. At that time the medieval city was beautified and modernized with new houses and streets. The British traveler Arthur Young (1741–1820) remarked on this in the late 1780s: "Much as I had read and heard of the commerce, wealth, and magnificence of this city, they greatly surpassed my expectations. . . . The new houses that are building in all quarters of the town, mark, too clearly to be misunderstood, the prosperity of the place."[1]

The Museum's delightful small and intimate room is believed to have come from the Hôtel de Saint-Marc on the cours d'Albret, one of the recently laid out avenues. This residence was built between 1782 and 1784 by an unknown architect for the king's minister Joseph Dufour. It was named, however, after Jean-Paul-André des Rasins (also Razins), the marquis de Saint-Marc (1728–1818), who became its second owner in 1787, having purchased not only the building but also the mirrors, tapestries, and other interior decoration. Formerly an officer in the Régiment des Gardes Françaises, the marquis de Saint-Marc retired in 1762 and then devoted himself to writing scripts for

opera and ballet, poetry, and educational pieces for children. The presence of a circular room to the left of the entrance facing the courtyard of his mansion makes it plausible that the Museum's paneling was originally installed there. A dumbwaiter in the kitchen directly below suggests that the room may have been the setting for private dinner or supper parties. The walls are rhythmically divided by eight long and narrow panels flanking the double doors, wall niches, windows, and mirrors. Displaying arabesques consisting of trophies symbolic of various arts and farming and hunting, the carving on these panels—mostly in low relief—has been attributed to the local sculptor Barthélemy Cabirol and his workshop (see details, pages 44 and 45, above). Additional trophies are found above the lintel of the two

sets of doors—one, with a compass, T-square, and basket overgrown with acanthus leaves alluding to the origin of the Corinthian capital, is emblematic of architecture (see detail above).

Cabirol is known to have been responsible for high-quality *boiseries* in a number of private residences in Bordeaux. An engraving in César Daly's *Décorations intérieures empruntées à des édifices français* of 1880 (fig. 37) depicts this room with its original mantel and parquet floor. The latter was laid out in a radiating pattern that emphasized the shape of the room. Both the mantelpiece and the floor have since been replaced by other eighteenth-century examples.

1. Young 1792, pp. 45, 47.

References: Parker 1977, pp. 394–95, pl. XII, fig. 17; Kisluk-Grosheide 1996, ill.; Baumeister et al. 2009, pp. 205–8, figs. 5, 8.

9 (detail)

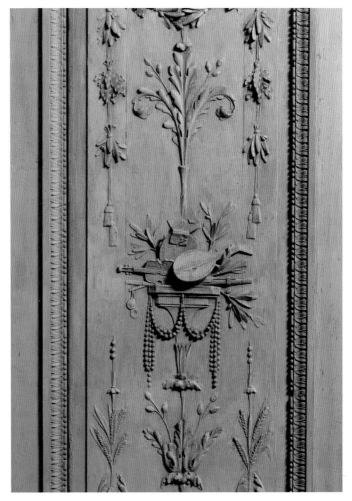

9 (detail)

Fig. 37. Engraving of the
Bordeaux Room, in César Daly,
*Décorations intérieures empruntées
à des édifices français*, vol. 2
(Paris, 1880), plate 41, where it
is described as "the salon of a
private house on the Cours
d'Albret in Bordeaux." The
Metropolitan Museum of Art,
New York, The Thomas J.
Watson Library.

Furniture

10. Cabinet on stand (*cabinet*)

Paris, ca. 1645 (with extensive alterations)
Oak and poplar veneered with ebony, stained
and natural ivory, bone, kingwood, amaranth
and other marquetry woods, and ebonized
pearwood; gilt-bronze capitals and bases; plated
iron hardware
H. 74½ in. (189.2 cm), w. 66 in. (167.6 cm),
d. 23 in. (58.4 cm)
Gift of Mrs. Harold Fowler, 1931 (31.66a,b)

This imposing cabinet on stand
belonged at one time to George Gor-
don Meade (1815–1872), the American
Civil War general who led the Union
troops to victory at the Battle of
Gettysburg. Largely veneered with
lustrous ebony, the architectural piece
bears eloquent testimony to the
importance to the European economy
of overseas trade. In the seventeenth
century, for the first time, tropical
timber and other exotic materials
became available in quantity to European cabinetmakers, who prospered
as they set new fashions in furniture.
Since imported wood was still a costly
commodity in mid-seventeenth-
century France, the unknown cabinetmaker carefully layered the nearly
black veneer on the cabinet's super-
structure to minimize the amount of
ebony needed. Furthermore, he used
blackened, so-called ebonized, pearwood for the lower part, which was,
after all, not at eye level. The exterior
is richly decorated with ripple moldings and engraved ornament and also
displays carved biblical scenes from
the Old Testament. Some of them,
such as Judith with the head of Holofernes (see detail above), are based on

Detail of the exterior
carving: *Judith with the
Head of Holofernes*

Fig. 38. *Judith with the Head
of Holofernes*, woodcut attributed to Jean Cousin the
Younger, in *Figures historiques
du Vieux Testament*, published
by Jean Le Clerc (Paris,
1614). The Metropolitan
Museum of Art, New York,
Harris Brisbane Dick Fund,
1931 (31.65).

Interior of the cabinet showing the *caisson*

woodcut illustrations from *Figures historiques du Vieux Testament* by Jean Le Clerc, first published in 1596 and then in a second edition of 1614 (see fig. 38). In addition, female personifications of faith, hope, and charity, the theological virtues, are represented in the niches on the cabinet's exterior, while two cardinal virtues, prudence and justice, are rendered on the interior doors. All the differently treated ebony surfaces reflect the light in various ways and give the object life.

In marked contrast with the monochromatic decor of the outside, the central compartment, or *caisson*, on the inside is brightly colored with marbleized and tinted ivory, bone, and various kinds of wood (see detail page 47, below). Treated as a sumptuous architectural interior, it was meant to surprise the viewer and enchant the eye. The use of mirror glass in the recess offers unexpected perspective views and allows a treasured object placed there to be seen and admired from different angles. Certain elements of this interior date to the late nineteenth century, when the cabinet underwent a major restoration by the leading New York cabinetmaking- and interior-decorating firm of Herter Brothers, whose name

and the date 1884–85 are stamped twice on the back.

With their numerous interior drawers, ebony cabinets of this kind were traditionally used for the safekeeping of jewelry, documents, and personal items. On December 23, 1779, Horace Walpole revealed to his friend Anne Liddell, Countess of Upper Ossory (ca. 1738–1804), how the marquise de Sévigné (1626–1696) had used her own cabinet, which by Walpole's time was quite an old-fashioned piece: "You are to know, Madam, that I have in my custody the individual ebony cabinet in which Madame de Sévigny kept her pens and paper for writing her matchless letters. . . . It wears, indeed, all the outward and visible signs of such venerable preciousness, for it is clumsy, cumbersome, and shattered, and inspires no more idea of her spirit and *légèreté*, than the mouldy thighbone of a saint does of the unction of his sermons."[1]

1. Walpole 1937–83, vol. 33 (1965), pp. 150–51.

References: Remington 1931, figs. 1–3, 5; Baumeister 2005; Daniëlle O. Kisluk-Grosheide in Kisluk-Grosheide, Koeppe, and Rieder 2006, pp. 34–37, no. 11, ill.

11. Table

Paris, ca. 1660
Attributed to Pierre Gole (ca. 1620–1684)
Oak and fruitwood veneered with tortoiseshell, stained and natural ivory, and other woods; gilt-bronze mounts
H. 30⅞ in. (78.4 cm), w. 41⅛ in. (104.6 cm), d. 27 in. (68.6 cm)
Gift of Mr. and Mrs. Charles Wrightsman, 1986 (1986.38.1)

Little is known of this table's history, and one can only wonder if the exquisite piece was among the many commissions that Pierre Gole, cabinetmaker to Louis XIV, received from the Crown. He is known to have supplied more than a hundred tables, often with a pair of matching candlestands, to the king and the court. Born in Bergen, the Netherlands, Gole was active in Paris during most of his working life. During the mid-1650s he began to specialize in a new and colorful type of veneer known as marquetry. For this decoration, Gole made extensive use of costly and exotic materials such as ebony, tortoiseshell, and ivory from such faraway places as Madagascar, the Indian Ocean, and Guinea. Supported on slender columnar legs, the rectangular top of this table is divided by bands of marquetry into different compartments somewhat resembling *pietra dura* (hardstone) mosaic works, which may have been its inspiration (see detail right). Inscribed in a four-lobed cartouche, a bouquet of flowers tied with a ribbon occupies the center. Intensifying the vivid color scheme and heightening the sense of naturalism, green-stained ivory was selected for the leaves of the flowers.

Top of the table

During the nineteenth century the table was part of the collections at Mentmore Towers, Buckinghamshire, England. Built for Baron Mayer Amschel de Rothschild (1818–1874), this stately Renaissance-style residence was richly furnished with French art. Elizabeth Rigby, later Lady Eastlake (1809–1893), described the house in 1872 as "a museum of everything, and not least of furniture, which is all in marquety, or *pietra dura*, or *vermeille*. I don't believe the Medici were so lodged in the height of their glory." [1]

1. Eastlake 1895, vol. 2, p. 224.

References: James Parker in Metropolitan Museum of Art 1986, pp. 28–29, ill.; Lunsingh Scheurleer 2005, pp. 90–91, 251, fig. 50 and ill. pp. 81, 251; Daniëlle O. Kisluk-Grosheide in Kisluk-Grosheide, Koeppe, and Rieder 2006, pp. 43–45, no. 14, ill.

12. Writing desk (*bureau brisé*)

Paris, ca. 1685
Designed and possibly engraved by Jean Bérain (1640–1711); made by Alexandre-Jean Oppenordt (1639–1715)
Oak, pine, and walnut veneered with ebony, rosewood, and marquetry of engraved brass and tortoiseshell; gilt-bronze mounts; steel hardware
H. 30⅜ in. (77.2 cm), w. 41¾ in. (106 cm), d. 23⅜ in. (59.4 cm)
Gift of Mrs. Charles Wrightsman, 1986 (1986.365.3)

With a folding top that lifts up to reveal a narrow writing surface, this desk is known in French as a *bureau brisé* (literally, "broken desk"). Introduced about 1669, this type of writing table remained fashionable until the early years of the eighteenth century, when it was replaced by the more practical, flat-topped *bureau plat*. The Museum's desk was commissioned with another almost identical example for Louis XIV's Petit Cabinet, a small private room in the north wing of the Château de Versailles, and is one of the few extant pieces of furniture made for the personal use of the Sun King.

The exterior is embellished with marquetry of tortoiseshell and engraved brass, known as Boulle work, after the French royal cabinetmaker André-Charles Boulle (1642–1732), who was a true master of the technique. A thin sheet of red-tinted tortoiseshell was laid atop a thin sheet of brass, and an intricate pattern was cut through both layers before they were separated. The Museum's desk received the more beautiful version of the decoration (so-called *première partie*), where the tortoiseshell forms the ground enriched with inlays of cutout brass. The pendant desk was

Top of the writing desk

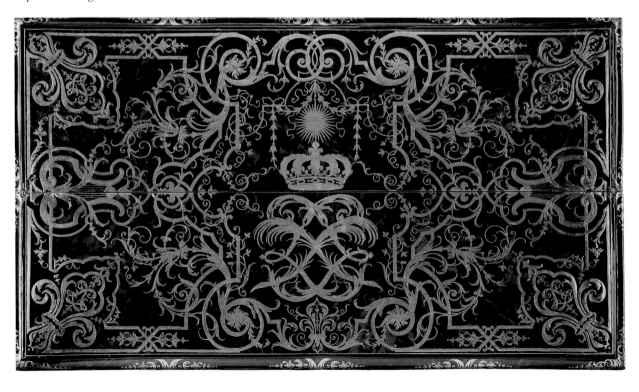

veneered with the "leftover" materials, consisting of a brass ground inlaid with cutout tortoiseshell (*contre partie*). Without wasting any of the exotic tortoiseshell or the metal, it was thus possible to produce an identical pair, with the distinction that the decoration of the one desk was the exact reverse of the other. Jean Bérain was responsible for the design of the resplendent marquetry, which was

executed by the Dutch-born cabinet-maker Alexandre-Jean Oppenordt, who on July 25, 1685, was paid 240 livres for his work.

Richly adorned with royal symbols, strapwork, and acanthus scrolls, the top of the *bureau brisé* shows in the center a sunburst—symbol of Apollo, the sun god, to whom Louis XIV likened himself—a crown, and a crossed-*L* monogram. Openwork

fleurs-de-lis (symbols of the French monarchy) inscribed with smaller crossed-*L* monograms embellish the corners. The hinged sections that allow the top to open are straddled by two lyres, the musical instrument of Apollo.

This very specific marquetry decoration and the overall measurements make it possible to identify this writing desk and its mate in a royal inventory drawn up in 1718 after Louis's death. Many pieces of furniture and furnishings made for the French court were sold during the French Revolution but this small writing desk and its pair had already left the royal collections during the ancien régime. Considered old-fashioned by the middle of the eighteenth century, they were auctioned off in July 1751 as two lots and appear to have led separate existences ever since. The Museum's *bureau brisé* was acquired by the cabinetmaker and furniture dealer Gilles Joubert (1689–1775) for 40 livres. Its subsequent history remains largely a mystery.

References: Ronfort 1986b, ill.; James Parker in Metropolitan Museum of Art 1987, pp. 27–28, ill.; James Parker in Parker et al. 1989, pp. 14–15, 64, ill.; Kisluk-Grosheide 2006, pp. 6–8, figs. 4–6; Wolfram Koeppe in Kisluk-Grosheide, Koeppe, and Rieder 2006, pp. 50–53, no. 17, ill.

13. Clock with pedestal

Paris, ca. 1690
Attributed to André-Charles Boulle (1642–1732), after designs by Jean Bérain (1640–1711); movement, probably by Isaac II Thuret (1630–1706)
Case and pedestal: oak veneered with tortoiseshell, engraved brass, and pewter; gilt-bronze mounts; gilt-brass dial with enameled numerals; brass and steel movement
H. 7 ft. 3¼ in. (222 cm); w. 13¾ in. (34.9 cm); d. 11⅜ in. (28.9 cm)
Rogers Fund, 1958 (58.53a–c)

The eight-day, spring-wound movement of this timepiece, signed "J. Thuret," was most likely the work of Isaac II Thuret, clockmaker to Louis XIV and a member of an important family of horologists. In May 1691 he organized a lottery with a repeater clock on a pedestal as first prize. This piece was fitted with a barometer and, in addition, was richly decorated with gilt bronze. It appears to have been very similar to the

Museum's clock and gives a good indication of its date. Just like the first prize in the lottery, the Museum's clock was intended to hold a barometer in its pedestal (see detail far right). Five inscriptions near the top alluding to various weather conditions, ranging from *tourment[e]* (tempest) to *tres sec* (very dry), form the perimeter of the dial of a barometer, although the piece appears never to have been used as such. The case and pedestal of the clock, ornamented with marquetry of tortoiseshell, brass, and pewter, have been attributed to the royal *ébéniste* André-Charles Boulle, "who makes a sort of *Mosaick* works extremely neat, and which the Curious preserve very choicely," according to Germain Brice's popular guidebook of 1687, *A New Description of Paris*.[1] Boulle is known to have made numerous clock

Clock dial (detail)

Barometer

cases in his workshop, which was housed in the Palais du Louvre, not far from the lodgings of the influential artist Jean Bérain. Some of Bérain's engraved designs were used for the decoration of this clock. There is a striking harmony between the ornament of the case and of the dial. The timepiece is surmounted by royal symbols in gilt bronze: a sunburst with a mask of the sun god Apollo, a crown, and a pair of lyres, as well as a pair of cornucopias, the traditional symbol of abundance. Although all these emblems clearly refer to the Sun King and his reign, no royal provenance for this clock has been established.

1. Brice 1687, pp. 20–21.

References: Parker 1960b, ill.; Ottomeyer and Pröschel 1986, vol. 1, p. 44, no. 1.41.1, ill.; Ronfort 1986a, pp. 483–85; James Parker in Parker et al. 1989, pp. 16–17, 64, ill.

14. Armchair (*fauteuil à la reine*)

Paris, ca. 1690–1710
Carved and gilded walnut; late 17th-century wool velvet (not original)
H. 46½ in. (118.1 cm), w. 28 in. (71.1 cm), d. 23¼ in. (59.1 cm)
Purchase, Gift of Mr. and Mrs. Charles Wrightsman, by exchange, 1983 (1983.526)

This armchair, with its gently curving frame and lack of stretchers strengthening the legs, anticipates the stylistic developments of the eighteenth century. It is a type with a flat back called *fauteuil à la reine* as opposed to the *fauteuil en cabriolet* sporting a slightly concave back, which was fashionable later, during the Louis XV period. The chief glory of this example is the elaborate decoration, which, in some ways, is closer to the art of the goldsmith than to that of the wood-carver. It has even been suggested that the large set to which the Museum's chair belonged, with its stylized lambrequin motifs "draped" over the arms and its delicate openwork ornament on the legs and on the rails that support the seat, may have been made to replace silver seat furniture at Versailles that was melted down by Louis XIV in 1689. While that cannot be verified, the armchair is among the earliest known pieces fitted with a drop-in back and seat, a style called *à châssis*, to facilitate the seasonal changing of the upholstery.

References: James Parker in Metropolitan Museum of Art 1984, p. 31, ill.; Wolfram Koeppe in Kisluk-Grosheide, Koeppe, and Rieder 2006, pp. 61–63, no. 21, ill.

15. Cabinet (*armoire*)

Paris, ca. 1700
Attributed to André-Charles Boulle (1642–1732)
Oak veneered with macassar and Gabon ebony, ebonized fruitwood, burl wood, and marquetry of tortoiseshell and brass; gilt-bronze mounts
H. 91¾ in. (233 cm), w. 48 in. (121.9 cm), d. 19 in. (48.3 cm)
Fletcher Fund, 1959 (59.108)

Describing the costly furnishings of the Parisian homes he had visited during his 1698 trip to France, Dr. Martin Lister (ca. 1638–1712) mentioned "*Cabinets* and *Bureaus* of Ivory inlaid with Tortoiseshell."[1] He may well have been thinking of some sumptuous pieces made in the atelier of Pierre Gole (see no. 11) or of André-Charles Boulle, cabinetmaker to Louis XIV since 1672. Boulle was by no means the only *ébéniste* to use marquetry of tortoiseshell and brass to embellish the surface of furniture and clock cases. But he was by far the most renowned cabinetmaker to work in that technique, which was named for him, and he was one of the few *ébénistes* identified by name in eighteenth-century sale catalogues.

This armoire is one of a group of imposing cabinets that reflect a design by Boulle now in the Musée des Arts Décoratifs, Paris (fig. 39). With a rich combination of *première partie* but mostly *contre partie* marquetry on the door panels and sides (see entry for no. 12), it shows an innovative use of gilt-bronze mounts typical of Boulle's output. Against established guild regulations, Boulle's cabinetry workshop also operated a foundry for casting, chasing, and gilding metal mounts. This craft was generally reserved for members of a different guild, but Boulle was exempt from these restrictions owing to the royal favor he enjoyed and the special lodgings granted to him at the Louvre. Corner mounts, hinges, handles, and escutcheons are protective and highly functional, but Boulle's exquisitely manufactured bronzes also added an element of sculpture to his furniture. On the Museum's cabinet the two-dimensional marquetry scrolls are beautifully set off by the three-dimensional mounts. The masks of mythological wind gods at the corners of the door panels, some with young, clean-shaven faces and others more mature with beards, not found in the drawing or on similar armoires by Boulle, may have been added at a later date (see detail below left).

1. Lister 1699, p. 9.

References: James Parker in Parker et al. 1989, pp. 18–19, 64, ill.; Wolfram Koeppe in Kisluk-Grosheide, Koeppe, and Rieder 2006, pp. 66–68, no. 23, ill.

Detail of the right door

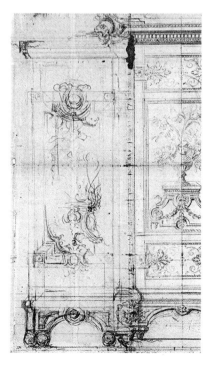

Fig. 39. André-Charles Boulle, *Design for a Cabinet* (detail). Sanguine and pen and ink. Musée des Arts Décoratifs, Paris.

16. Pair of folding stools (*pliants*)

Paris, ca. 1735–39
Carved and gilded walnut; silk velvet with gold
trim (not original)
H. 17¾ in. (45.1 cm), w. 23 in. (58.4 cm),
d. 16½ in. (41.9 cm)
Gift of Mr. and Mrs. Charles Wrightsman, 1971
(1971.206.9, 10)

Stools played an important role in the hierarchical seating arrangements of the French court, which followed a strict and complex protocol. Depending on the rank of the company—which would include members of the royal family, courtiers, and dignitaries—one remained standing or was assigned a floor cushion (*carreau*), stool, or, rarely, a side chair. Armchairs were reserved for the king and the queen. Large numbers of stools were listed in the royal inventories; one type, called *pliant*, which includes the present pair, had an X-shaped frame that could conveniently be folded.

The inventory mark of the palace of Versailles, an interlaced double *V* and a closed crown, is stamped underneath the lower struts of the Museum's stools (see detail right). Even though the authenticity of these marks has been questioned, the excellent quality of the work, expressed not only in the carving but also in the recutting (*reparure*) of the gesso, leaves no doubt that this pair belonged to an important set of seat furniture.

Consisting of calcium carbonate mixed with rabbit glue, gesso or whiting forms the base coat for the gilding. After it has been applied to a carved frame and has dried, this layer needs to be recut to restore detail or definition to the decoration. Motifs or ground patterns too delicate to be cut into the wood itself, such as the diaper design on the Museum's stools, were also added during the *reparure*. Despite the fact that the appearance of these low seats depended largely on the richness of the upholstery and trimmings of their cushions, the frames of the stools were elaborately carved with Rococo ornament. The shaped outline of the supports is enlivened with bulrushes, basket-weave motifs, and partly open-worked acanthus leaves. Large rosettes cover the bolts that allow the stools to fold.

References: Verlet 1963, p. 161, no. 29, pl. IV; Watson 1966b, pp. 72–75, no. 50a, b, ill.; Kisluk-Grosheide 2006, p. 13, fig. 14.

Inventory marks

17. Pair of corner cabinets (*encoignures*)

Paris, ca. 1745–49
Bernard II van Risenburgh (ca. 1696–ca. 1767)
Oak veneered with ebony and Coromandel lacquer, cherry wood, and purplewood; gilt-bronze mounts; brocatelle marble top
H. 35⅞ in. (91.1 cm), w. 33⅞ in. (86 cm), d. 26⅛ in. (66.4 cm)
Gift of Mr. and Mrs. Charles Wrightsman, 1983 (1983.185.1a,b, 2a,b)

In January 1750 and April 1751, the Parisian *marchand-mercier* Lazare Duvaux (ca. 1703–1758) sold two pairs of corner cabinets for 580 and 650 livres, respectively.[1] Veneered with Coromandel lacquer and mounted with gilt bronze, they were fitted with Antin marble tops. Although the descriptions are too brief to permit a positive identification with the Museum's pair, whose tops, moreover, are of a different type of marble (perhaps replacements), these entries in the famous dealer's account book offer a good idea of the considerable cost of such corner cabinets. Furthermore, based on his sale records for the period 1748–53, it appears there was a demand for case furniture embellished with Coromandel lacquer. Duvaux sold several such pieces to his frequent customer Madame de Pompadour, the king's mistress. Distinguished by designs that are not painted on the surface but incised and filled with colored lacquer, objects decorated in this Chinese technique were shipped to Europe by way of the Coromandel coast of southeast India, hence the name.

The Parisian furniture maker Bernard II van Risenburgh, who stamped both pieces, made a number of corner cabinets fitted with either a single door or a double set of doors, depending on the size of the Asian lacquer panels made available to him by the *marchand-mercier*. In this case, he used tall and narrow pieces cut from a large multileaf Coromandel screen—which explains why the scenes on the doors are not continuous. As if it were a single panel, the lacquer is framed by sinuous Rococo-style gilt-bronze mounts incorporating C-scrolls and floral trails. The mounts appear to have been cast as one piece but, in fact, they consist of a number of different elements that overlap, some of which are stamped with the crowned-*C* tax mark. Based on these marks (the *C* stands for *cuivre*, or copper, the main ingredient of bronze), the mounts can be dated between February 1745 and February 1749, when this tax, imposed by a royal edict, was in effect. Any piece of decorative bronze above a certain weight sold during that period had to be struck with the crowned-*C* stamp to show that duty had been paid. Mounts like this are found on other pieces by Van Risenburgh, as well; the cartouche-shaped mount on the central leg is a later addition.

1. Duvaux 1748–58/1965, vol. 2, pp. 40, 80.

References: Watson 1966b, pp. 170–74, no. 100a, b, ill.; Impey and Kisluk-Grosheide 1994, pp. 55–56, fig. 16; Rieder 1994, pp. 37, 39, fig. 14; Wolvesperges 2000, p. 263, ill. no. 133.

18. Armchair
(*fauteuil à la reine*)

Paris, ca. 1749
Attributed to Nicolas-Quinibert Foliot
(1706–1776), possibly after a design by Pierre
Contant d'Ivry (1698–1777)
Carved and gilded oak; silk velvet with gold trim
H. 43½ in. (110.5 cm), w. 31½ in. (80 cm),
d. 27½ in. (69.9 cm)
Gift of J. Pierpont Morgan, 1907 (07.225.57)

The French statesman René-Louis de Voyer de Paulmy (1694–1757), marquis d'Argenson, observed in 1749 that the palace at Parma was bereft of everything; it had not a stick of furniture nor even a staircase. He predicted that much time would be needed to remedy these shortcomings.[1] No wonder, then, that the previous year Louise-Élisabeth, the eldest and favorite daughter of Louis XV, who with her husband, Don Philip of Spain, had been awarded the duchy of Parma, declined to settle in the empty shell. She traveled to her father's court at Versailles instead, where she commissioned furnishings for her new home. Louise-Élisabeth (1727–1759) returned to northern Italy in October with thirty-four wagonloads of purchases and gifts. It is quite possible that this armchair was among the things she brought back at that time.

Part of a large set of seat furniture made in Paris but assembled, gilded, and upholstered in Parma, this chair has been attributed to Nicolas-Quinibert Foliot and was possibly executed after a design by the architect and designer Pierre Contant d'Ivry. The Foliots were an important family of chairmakers active in mid-eighteenth-century Paris and employed by the Garde-Meuble de la Couronne, the royal office that supplied furniture to the French court.

An unknown sculptor executed the high-relief carving, consisting of rocailles, shells, wing motifs, C-scrolls, and floral garlands. This decoration is highly asymmetrical on the chair's side rails and is thus an expression of the pure Rococo style. The chair is upholstered *à châssis*, with a drop-in seat and removable back and arm pads, to which the original crimson velvet is tacked underneath, accommodating a seasonal change of upholstery. The scalloped edge of the gold trim echoes the serpentine outline of the chair's frame. An armchair belonging to the same set is shown in the Museum's full-length portrait of Louise-Élisabeth's daughter Maria Luisa of Parma (1751–1819), later queen of Spain (no. 89).

1. Journal entry for March 30, 1749, in Argenson 1857–58, vol. 3, p. 252.

References: Parker 1966, pp. 179, 182, figs. 1, 3; Pallot 1995, ill. nos. 5, 7; Daniëlle O. Kisluk-Grosheide in Kisluk-Grosheide, Koeppe, and Rieder 2006, pp. 119–22, no. 46, ill.

19. Bedside table
(*table de nuit*)

Paris, ca. 1750–56
Attributed to Bernard II van Risenburgh
(ca. 1696–ca. 1767)
Oak veneered with tulipwood and kingwood;
gilt-bronze mounts; Sarrancolin marble; silk
moiré drawer lining (not original)
H. 30¼ in. (78.1 cm), w. 20½ in. (52.1 cm),
w. 14¼ in. (36.2 cm)
Gift of Mr. and Mrs. Charles Wrightsman, 1985
(1985.313.1)

*From hence we went forward to Belle
Vue, the finest Situation I have
hitherto seen in France—the House
perfectly elegant;—it was inhabited by
Madame de Pompadour it seems,
when in the plenitude of her Power.*

—Hester Thrale, journal entry for
October 26, 1775

Situated between Meudon and Saint-Cloud, the Château de Bellevue, as its name suggests, offered beautiful prospects over the Seine River to the panorama of Paris in the distance. In 1750 Louis XV transferred the house, then just completed, to his official mistress, the marquise de Pompadour. Although modest in scale, the country residence was richly furnished by the king's favorite, who was born Jeanne-Antoinette Poisson (1721–1764), a commoner who became a great patron of the arts. The mark of the Château de Bellevue (*BV* under a crown) and the number 59 on the frame of this night table identify it as a piece listed in an inventory drawn up in 1763, six years after Louis XV had repurchased Bellevue and its furnishings from Madame de Pompadour. A number of such practical pieces of furniture intended to hold a chamber pot and other objects required during the night were acquired by Madame de Pompadour from the luxury dealer Lazare Duvaux between 1750 and 1756. An entry in Duvaux's account book for the years 1748–58 mentions that she purchased a pair of *tables de nuit* veneered with tulipwood and mounted with gilt bronze; they are described as being *à contours*, presumably referring to a serpentine outline,[1] such as the sinuous line of the railing along the top of this table and the subtle undulation of its sides, legs, and apertures.

Attributed to Bernard II van Risenburgh, this table shows the stylized floral marquetry of dark, end-cut wood—here kingwood—against a lighter tulipwood ground for which this highly talented cabinetmaker was justly famous. The gilt-bronze handles on the sides facilitated placing the table next to a bed at night and removing it to an adjacent room, the *garde-robe*, during the day. The marble shelves would protect the wood from any spillage, and the opening at the back provided extra ventilation. The table remained at Bellevue after Louis XVI gave the country residence and its contents to his three unmarried aunts, the princesses Adélaïde (1732–1800), Victoire (1733–1799), and Sophie (1734–1782). It was sold with the rest of the furnishings from Bellevue during the Revolution, in 1794.

Epigraph. Thrale 1775/1932, pp. 141–42.

1. Duvaux 1748–58/1965, vol. 2, p. 295.

References: Watson 1966b, pp. 204–7, no. 109, ill.; Verlet 1994, pp. 114–16, 259, no. 3, ill.; Kisluk-Grosheide 2006, pp. 32–33, fig. 44.

20, 21. Settee (*canapé*) and armchair (*fauteuil à la reine*)

Paris, 1754–56
Nicolas-Quinibert Foliot (1706–1776), probably
after designs by Pierre Contant d'Ivry
(1698–1777)
Carved and gilded beech; wool and silk tapestry
made at the Beauvais Manufactory
Settee
H. 44 in. (111.8 cm); w. 92½ in. (235 cm); d. 32 in.
(81.3 cm)
Gift of John D. Rockefeller Jr., 1935 (frame:
35.145.1); (tapestries: 35.145.15a–d)
Armchair
H. 41⅞ in. (106.4 cm); w. 30½ in. (77.5 cm),
d. 25½ in. (64.8 cm)
Purchase, Martha Baird Rockefeller Gift, 1966
(frame: 66.60.2); Gift of John D. Rockefeller Jr.,
1935 (tapestries: 35.145.23c–d, 25b, 26a)

Baron Johann Ernst Bernstorff
(1712–1772) served as Danish ambassador to the court of Versailles
between 1744 and 1751. According to
Charles-Philippe d'Albert, duc de
Luynes (1695–1758), the diplomat was
youthful and witty, possessed both
finesse and taste, and spoke the
French language better than many
native speakers.[1] During his stay in
France, Bernstorff formed many
friendships and developed a marked
taste for the French way of life. It
was, therefore, with reluctance that
he left Paris and returned to Denmark
in 1751 to assume the post of minister
of foreign affairs.

For the tapestry room of his newly
built residence in Copenhagen, he

acquired a series of four wall hangings,
Les Amours des Dieux (The Loves of
the Gods), from the Beauvais Manufactory. Covers for a set of twelve
armchairs and two settees (all of
which are in the Museum's collection)
were woven at the same time to complement the tapestries. They display
lighthearted compositions of animals,
birds, and flowers based on designs
by Jean-Baptiste Oudry (1686–1755).
The frames of the seat furniture were
made by the Parisian *menuisier*
Nicolas-Quinibert Foliot, who, like
his father, Nicolas Foliot, was furniture maker to the king's household.
Eight of the twelve chairs and one of
the settees are stamped with his name.
Enriched with symmetrically placed

Fig. 40. Kristian Zahrtmann, *The Tapestry Room at Bernstorff Palace*, 1881. Oil on canvas. Statens Museum for Kunst, Copenhagen.

Rococo ornament, floral garlands, palm branches, and a large shell motif centered on the crest rail, the undulating outline of the chairs and settees is echoed in the tapestry covers. Arranged along the walls, these pieces formed an integral aspect of the interior decoration of the room, which was furnished by Bernstorff according to the latest French fashion with console tables, mirrors, and gilt bronzes, all acquired in Paris (see fig. 40).

The tapestry room remained intact until the early twentieth century, when George I of the Hellenes (1845–1913), second son of King Christian IX of Denmark, was the owner of Bernstorff Palace. The crowned-*G* mark branded in the wooden frames of the chairs and settees identify the pieces as his property. He sold the tapestries and the seat furniture separately, and by 1902 the American

financier and collector J. Pierpont Morgan had acquired the chairs and settees for use in his London town house. There, during a visit in 1908 and much to their surprise, Queen Alexandra of England (1844–1925) and her sister Dowager Empress Maria Feodorovna of Russia (1847–1928), both Danish princesses, recognized the pieces as having belonged to their brother George. One of them exclaimed, "Why, there are the chairs . . . our brother had those chairs but they disappeared and we never knew what had become of them; they must have been sold."[2]

1. Luynes 1735–58/1860–65, vol. 6, p. 452.
2. Taylor 1957, p. 24.

References: Parker 1973, figs. 16–22; Standen 1985, vol. 2, pp. 484–98, no. 74, ill.; Pallot 1987, pp. 164, 166–69; Daniëlle O. Kisluk-Grosheide in Kisluk-Grosheide, Koeppe, and Rieder 2006, pp. 129–31, no. 50, ill.

22. Writing table (*table à écrire*)

Paris, ca. 1755
Bernard II van Risenburgh (ca. 1696–ca. 1767)
Oak veneered with tulipwood, kingwood, amaranth, mahogany, ebony, mother-of-pearl, and stained horn; gilt-bronze mounts; modern velvet
H. 30¾ in. (78.1 cm), w. 38 in. (96.5 cm), d. 22⅝ in. (57.5 cm)
Gift of Mr. and Mrs. Charles Wrightsman, 1976 (1976.155.100)

Letter writing was a much-practiced activity in eighteenth-century Europe. Horace Walpole, a prolific correspondent himself, reported on September 12, 1775, to his friend Anne Liddell, "There have been known here [in Paris] persons who wrote to one another four times a day; and I was told of one couple, who being always together, and the lover being fond of writing, he placed a screen between them, and then wrote to Madame on t'other side, and flung them over."[1] In order to accommodate this incessant writing, a variety of *tables à écrire*, large and small, were created. Often fitted with a leather- or velvet-covered writing surface, and with one or more drawers for the storage of quills and other paraphernalia, these pieces were generally placed in the private rooms of the house. This particularly elegant table is fitted with three pull-out shelves. One at the front encloses a shaped panel of green velvet; two smaller ones at either end, veneered with tulipwood, may have been used for taking dictation. The gilt-bronze gallery emphasizes the serpentine shape of the table's top (see detail right) and also prevents papers from sliding off.

Top of the writing table

Known for his stylized floral marquetry of end-cut woods, as seen on the main writing slide, Van Risenburgh rarely relied, as he did here, on colorful inlays of engraved mother-of-pearl and tinted horn. Considered one of the most talented *ébénistes* active during the reign of Louis XV, Van Risenburgh, who was both the son and father of cabinetmakers of the same name, stamped many of his pieces, including this one, with his initials *B.V.R.B.*

1. Walpole 1937–83, vol. 32 (1965), p. 263.

References: Watson 1966c, pp. 306–9, no. 151, ill.; Rieder 1994, p. 34, pls. I, II; Daniëlle O. Kisluk-Grosheide in Kisluk-Grosheide, Koeppe, and Rieder 2006, pp. 132–33, no. 51, ill.

23. Side table (*commode en console*)

Paris, ca. 1755–60
Bernard II van Risenburgh (ca. 1696–ca. 1767)
Oak and pine lacquered black and veneered with 17th-century Japanese lacquer; gilt-bronze mounts; Sarrancolin marble top
H. 35½ in. (90.2 cm), w. 37½ in. (95.3 cm), d. 21 in. (53.3 cm)
Gift of Mr. and Mrs. Charles Wrightsman, 1976 (1976.155.101)

Fitted with one drawer in its frieze, this sophisticated piece is a combination of a console table—designed to be placed against a wall—and a commode—a chest of drawers—as is clearly illustrated by its French name, *commode en console*. Only a few such tables are known today, and they appear to have been fashionable for but a short period during the middle of the eighteenth century; five were recorded in the account book of the *marchand-mercier* Lazare Duvaux between December 1753 and February 1757. The most expensive of them, mounted with lacquer and decorated with gilt bronze, was sold on May 13, 1756, for 1,150 livres.[1] Since no other example with lacquer is known to exist, this entry in Duvaux's book may describe the Museum's table—but very little else can be said about its history.

Although console tables were generally made by those joiners who specialized in wall paneling or *boiserie* (see page 24) this piece was, like most commodes, the work of an *ébéniste* versed in the art of veneering. Bernard II van Risenburgh, whose initials are stamped on the top and underneath the carcase, worked almost exclusively for *marchands-merciers* such as Duvaux, Thomas-Joachim Hébert (d. 1773), and Simon-Philippe Poirier (ca. 1720–1785). One of the dealers could have supplied him with the Japanese lacquer for this table, probably obtained from seventeenth-century cabinets. A detailed description of the best way to process and handle Asian lacquer for use on European furniture was published by André-Jacob Roubo in his treatise *L'Art du menuisier* of 1769–75. Roubo indicated how the lacquer should be cut from its wooden substrate in order not to crack it and then how to heat and glue it to the body of a new piece of furniture. He also suggested framing the lacquer with gilt-bronze mounts to mask the joints and hide any chipping that might have occurred during the cutting process—as has been beautifully done by Van Risenburgh on the Museum's table.[2]

1. Duvaux 1748–58/1965, vol. 2, p. 281.
2. Roubo 1769–75, vol. 3, pt. 3 (1774), pp. 1020–21.

References: Watson 1966b, pp. 226–29, no. 118, ill.; Rieder 1994, p. 37, pl. III; Daniëlle O. Kisluk-Grosheide in Kisluk-Grosheide, Koeppe, and Rieder 2006, pp. 142–43, no. 56, ill.

24. Folding card table (*table de jeu brisée en angle*)

Paris, ca. 1755–65
Attributed to Bernard II van Risenburgh
(ca. 1696–ca. 1767)
Oak veneered with tulipwood, amaranth, kingwood, and *bois* satiné; walnut drawer; gilt-bronze
mounts; brass molding; modern silk velvet
H. 27⅝ in. (70.2 cm), w. 42⅜ in. (107.7 cm),
d. 21¾ in. (53.3 cm)
Gift of Mr. and Mrs. Charles Wrightsman, 1983
(1983.185.3)

*In mentioning cards, I ought to
observe, that . . . [the French] learn to
play not barely for amusement, but
also with a view to advantage; and,
indeed, you seldom meet with a native
of France, whether male or female,
who is not a complete gamester, well
versed in all the subtleties and finesses
of the art.*

—Tobias Smollett, *Travels through France
and Italy*

As gaming was the principal indoor diversion of eighteenth-century France, a variety of tables was created, often for specific games like three-handed ombre or tri, piquet, or brelan. A description of one example in Lazare Duvaux's account book suggests that this elegant folding table was used for quadrille. On August 9, 1753, the dealer sold a solid mahogany quadrille table "brisée en angle" (folding on the diagonal), embellished with gilt bronze, and lined with cloth, to Madame de Pompadour for 85 livres.[1]

When closed, the Museum's table has a triangular shape and forms a synthesis of sinuous lines, echoed by the double curve of the cabriole legs. One of these S-shaped legs can be pulled backward to support the hinged top when unfolded. A shallow walnut drawer for storage of game essentials is recessed on top of this sliding leg. The rounded corners of the open top could be used for discarded cards and counters or for the placement of candlesticks to offer the players light on their game. Although not stamped, this table has been attributed to Bernard II van Risenburgh, based on the high quality of its tulipwood marquetry inlaid with floral and foliated sprays of end-cut kingwood.

Epigraph. Smollett 1766/1969, p. 72.

1. Duvaux 1748–58/1965, vol. 2, p. 166.

References: Watson 1966b, pp. 222–23, no. 116, ill.; Rieder 1994, pp. 34–35, figs. 3, 4.

25. Writing table (*bureau plat*)

Paris, 1759
Gilles Joubert (1689–1775)
Lacquered oak; gilt-bronze mounts; leather
(not original)
H. 31⅞ in. (80.7 cm), w. 69¼ in. (175.9 cm),
d. 36 in. (91.4 cm)
Gift of Mr. and Mrs. Charles Wrightsman, 1973
(1973.315.1)

In his *Useful Hints to Those Who
Make the Tour of France*, which
appeared in 1768, Philip Thicknesse
(1719–1792) expressed the opinion
that Louis XV would have made a
much better country gentleman than
a sovereign prince, since he loved
the diversions of country life and
seldom went to Paris.[1] It is not surprising, then, that the king spent
much of his time at Versailles, where
daily business was conducted in his
Cabinet Intérieur. This small study,
its windows overlooking the palace
courtyard below, was one of the most
beautiful rooms of his private apartment. On December 29, 1759, Gilles
Joubert supplied this writing table, a
so-called *bureau plat*, or flat-topped
desk, lacquered in brilliant crimson
and with pseudo-Asian landscape
scenes in gold for the king's use in
the Cabinet Intérieur. The surface
decoration imitates red and gold
Chinese lacquer, which was fashionable in France as veneer for furniture
in the middle of the eighteenth century.
Joubert, who had been appointed
cabinetmaker to the Garde-Meuble
de la Couronne in 1758 and became
cabinetmaker to the king in 1763,
had a long and successful career that
included numerous royal commissions. In fact, he received so many
orders from the Crown that he often

Right front corner of the writing table

needed the assistance of other crafts-men to fulfill them.

The partly pierced gilt-bronze mounts not only emphasize the grace-ful curving lines of the writing table but also protect and frame the lustrous lacquered surface (see detail left). The flat top, originally lined with black velvet, allowed the king and his min-isters to spread out a multitude of documents and unfold maps. The *bureau plat* remained in the same room under Louis XV's grandson and successor, Louis XVI, until December 1786, when it was replaced by a new marquetry writing table by Guillaume Benneman (d. 1811). Joubert's piece was passed along to the king's brother, the comte de Provence, later Louis XVIII, for whom it was restored in 1787. The writing table stayed at Versailles until the Revolu-tionary sales of royal property in 1793–94.

1. Thicknesse 1768, p. 67.

References: Francis J. B. Watson in Watson and Dauterman 1970, pp. 42–51, no. 296, ill.; Verlet 1990, pp. 48–51, no. 6, ill.; Kisluk-Grosheide 2006, pp. 13–14, figs. 15, 16; Daniëlle O. Kisluk-Grosheide in Kisluk-Grosheide, Koeppe, and Rieder 2006, pp. 144–46, no. 57, ill.

Inventory number of the Garde-Meuble de la Couronne painted underneath the top of the writing table

26. Small writing desk (*bonheur-du-jour*)

Paris, 1768
Attributed to Martin Carlin (ca. 1730–1785);
twelve plaques painted by Denis Levé (active
1754–1805)
Oak veneered with tulipwood, amaranth, and
stained sycamore; mahogany; seventeen Sèvres
soft-paste porcelain plaques; gilt-bronze mounts;
velvet (not original)
H. 32½ in. (82.6 cm), w. 25⅞ in. (65.7 cm),
d. 16 in. (40.6 cm)
Gift of Samuel H. Kress Foundation, 1958
(58.75.48)

Madame du Barry (née Jeanne Bécu;
1743–1793) became the official mistress of Louis XV after the death of
Madame de Pompadour. In 1770 she
was described in less than favorable
terms by Elizabeth Seymour Percy,
Duchess of Northumberland (1716–
1776): "She is rather of a tall, middle
size, full breasted, and is pretty but
not to be call'd handsome . . . & has a
strong Look of her former profession.
Her Complexion is fair & clear & her
skin very smooth but her Bloom is
entirely gone off. . . . She is lodged in
parts of the Kings apartment in the
Attic."[1] Madame du Barry bought
luxury furnishings from the dealer
Simon-Philippe Poirier for those
private rooms at Versailles, including
a small writing table with a raised
section at the back, on November 18,
1768. It was recorded in her apartment at the palace, which she occupied until a few days before the king's
death, in May 1774, and described as
"a very pretty stepped table with
French porcelain on a green ground
with floral cartouches." Quite possibly the Museum's *bonheur-du-jour*, as
this type of small writing desk is
called, was the one formerly in the
possession of the king's favorite. The

model was repeated a number of times,
and today eleven such *bonheurs-du-
jour* are known, but this is the only
one that can be dated to 1768, based
on the date letter *P* for that year
painted on the back of twelve of the
porcelain plaques. The desk has been
attributed to Martin Carlin, who
made some eighty pieces of porcelain-
mounted furniture between 1765 and
1778, intended for a fashionable and
distinguished clientele consisting
mostly of aristocratic ladies. Carlin
supplied furniture to Poirier and
later to his partner and successor,
Dominique Daguerre (d. 1796), who
were the principal buyers of porcelain

plaques at the Sèvres manufactory.
Supported on four slender cabriole
legs, this small piece is fitted with a
single drawer in the frieze of the
lower section, which has a hinged
writing surface as well as a compartment that used to hold an inkwell, a
trough for a sponge, and a box for
sand to blot up excess ink.

1. Diary entry for May 16, 1770, in
   Northumberland 1752–74/1926, pp. 116–17.

References: James Parker and Carl Christian
Dauterman in Dauterman, Parker, and
Standen 1964, pp. 134–37, no. 22, figs. 104,
105; Baulez 1992, p. 45; Kisluk-Grosheide
2006, pp. 14–15, fig. 19; Daniëlle O. Kisluk-
Grosheide in Kisluk-Grosheide, Koeppe, and
Rieder 2006, pp. 156–58, no. 63, ill.

27. Barometer and thermometer

Paris, 1769
Works by Claude-Siméon Passemant
(1702–1769)
Oak; gilt-bronze mounts; glass; enamel;
three Sèvres soft-paste porcelain plaques
H. 40¾ in. (103.5 cm), w. 11 in. (27.9 cm),
d. 3⅜ in. (8.6 cm)
Gift of Samuel H. Kress Foundation, 1958
(58.75.59)

The scenes displayed on the Sèvres porcelain plaques of this instrument were inspired by a rare astronomical event that occurred twice during the eighteenth century. The second transit of the planet Venus across the sun took place on June 3, 1769, and was observed by the French court from the terraces of the Château de Saint-Hubert. Louis XV himself explained the phenomenon to Madame du Barry, lending her his telescope. This public display of favor did not go unnoticed and was quickly immortalized in a popular poem. Later that same year, on December 20, 1769, Madame du Barry acquired from the dealer Simon-Philippe Poirier a barometer and thermometer made by Claude-Siméon Passemant, engineer to the king. Mounted with Sèvres porcelain and gilt bronze, that piece is believed to be the one in the Museum's collection. Not only is the porcelain marked on the back with the date letter *Q*, for 1769, but also one of the plaques is inscribed "Passage de Venus sur le disque du [soleil] Juin 1769."

Madame du Barry appears to have kept the instrument as a souvenir of her triumph at Versailles. It may have been seen there by Henry Swinburne (1743–1803), who described visiting Du Barry's rooms tucked away above the apartment of the king on April 30, 1774, shortly before the latter's death: "We climbed up a dark winding stair-case, which I should have suspected would have led to an apartment of the Bastile [*sic*], rather than to the temple of love and elegance. In a low entresol we found the favourite sultana in her morning gown . . . and her hair undressed; she was very gracious, and chatted a good deal."[1] Several days later, as the king lay dying, Madame du Barry left Versailles and ultimately retired to her pavilion at Louveciennes. The barometer was sent there as well, as it was listed among the group of her possessions that were confiscated and returned to Paris after she was executed in 1793, a victim of the Terror.

1. Henry Swinburne to Edward Swinburne, April 30, 1774, in Swinburne 1774–1803/1900, vol. 1, p. 12.

References: James Parker and Carl Christian Dauterman in Dauterman, Parker, and Standen 1964, pp. 261–65, no. 63, figs. 221, 222; Baulez 1992, pp. 45–46, ill.; Kisluk-Grosheide 2006, pp. 16–17, figs. 20, 21.

28. Jewel coffer on stand (*coffre à bijoux*)

Paris, 1770
Attributed to Martin Carlin (ca. 1730–1785);
seven plaques painted by Jean-Jacques Pierre the
Younger (b. 1745/46) and one by Michel-Gabriel
Commelin (1746–1802)
Oak veneered with tulipwood, amaranth, stained
sycamore, holly, and ebonized holly; thirteen
Sèvres soft-paste porcelain plaques; gilt-bronze
mounts; modern velvet
H. 37½ in. (95.3 cm), w. 21⅞ in. (55.3 cm),
d. 14½ in. (36.8 cm)
Gift of Samuel H. Kress Foundation, 1958
(58.75.41)

In 1770, the year the Austrian arch-duchess Marie-Antoinette (1755–1793) married Louis-Auguste, the dauphin of France, she received among her wedding presents a jewel coffer on stand mounted with porcelain plaques. That piece (Château de Versailles) appears to have been the prototype for the eight other examples of this model known today, three of which are in the Museum's collection.[1] Made by or attributed to Martin Carlin, these coffers were marketed by Simon-Philippe Poirier, who himself may have invented their design, or by his partner and successor, Dominique Daguerre. All of them have a drawer in the stand fitted with a velvet-lined surface and a compartment for writing implements, so they must have doubled as a small desk. Although most of the plaques on the present example display floral decoration, the oval plaque on the lid and the shaped and undulating one on the front of the coffer show love symbols. Since most of the plaques are marked with the date letter *R* for the year 1770, it may be assumed that this piece of furniture was made then. Poirier delivered a coffer of French porcelain on a green

ground with floral cartouches, richly embellished with gilt bronze, and its stand, to Madame du Barry on December 13, 1770. Since the casket is not listed in any of the inventories of her belongings, it is possible that she ordered it as a sumptuous present for someone else. Coffers of this description were in the possession of Marie-Joséphine-Louise of Savoy, comtesse de Provence (1753–1810),

and of Empress Maria Feodorovna (1759–1828) at Pavlovsk.

1. The other two are acc. nos. 58.75.42 and 1976.155.109.

References: James Parker and Carl Christian Dauterman in Dauterman, Parker, and Standen 1964, pp. 126–32, no. 20, figs. 96–98, 100; Baulez 1992, p. 46; Kisluk-Grosheide 2006, p. 17, figs. 23, 24; Daniëlle O. Kisluk-Grosheide in Kisluk-Grosheide, Koeppe, and Rieder 2006, pp. 162–64, no. 67, ill.

29. Drop-front secretary on stand (*secrétaire à abattant* or *secrétaire en cabinet*)

Paris, ca. 1773
Martin Carlin (ca. 1730–1785); plaques decorated by Nicolas Bulidon (active 1763–92), Guillaume Noël (1734/35–1804), and Jacques-François Micaud the Elder (1732/35–1811)
Oak veneered with tulipwood, amaranth, holly, and ebonized holly; ten Sèvres soft-paste porcelain plaques; gilt-bronze mounts; marble; velvet (not original)
H. 47 in. (119.4 cm), w. 31¾ in. (80.7 cm), d. 17¾ in. (45.1 cm)
Gift of Samuel H. Kress Foundation, 1958 (58.75.44)

Madame du Barry appears to have had an insatiable taste for furniture embellished with porcelain plaques. Between 1768 and 1774 she acquired ten such pieces from Simon-Philippe Poirier. On December 30, 1773, the dealer sold his frequent client a secretary with French porcelain on a green ground lavishly decorated with gilt-bronze mounts, a description that matches the Museum's piece. Furthermore, the Sèvres plaques attached to the front and sides are marked with the letter *U* for the year 1773, making that an even more plausible date for this secretary, which is stamped by Martin Carlin.

Madame du Barry does not appear to have kept this desk for her personal use. Herself the recipient of magnificent gifts, the king's favorite seems to have been generous to others. She may have offered this particular piece as a wedding gift to Marie-Thérèse of Savoy (1756–1805), who married the comte d'Artois, the future Charles X of France, in November 1773. Among the belongings of the comtesse d'Artois seized by the Revolutionary government at Versailles in 1795 was a similar secretary. Although the

dimensions of the countess's piece match those of the Museum's secretary, the ground color of the Sèvres plaques is not mentioned in the list of confiscated furniture. For that reason it may never be possible to establish a royal provenance for the Museum's example, especially since at least one nearly identical secretary is extant.

The two oval compositions on the front showing baskets spilling over with lovely garden flowers are the work of Jacques-François Micaud, one of the floral painters at Sèvres

known to have decorated differently shaped plaques for furniture. The large number of high-quality gilt-bronze mounts lends this piece a sumptuous air. Access to the interior of the secretary appears to be given by a pair of doors, but it is actually fitted with a fall front that lowers to form a writing surface, also revealing the multiple drawers and pigeonholes inside. This type of desk is called *secrétaire à abattant* (drop-front secretary) or *secrétaire en cabinet* (secretary on an open support or stand).

That the interior of a closed secretary could awaken the curiosity of visitors is illustrated by an amusing passage in one of the letters of Marie-Anne de Vichy-Chamrond, marquise du Deffand (1697–1780), to Horace Walpole. On June 3, 1766, she regaled him with the story of two friends of Madame de Beuvron who had seen a pretty desk in the boudoir of their hostess. Desiring to know what it was like inside, the ladies used their own keys to try to open the piece but one of them broke in the lock. They begged a valet whom they suspected of having witnessed their action not to betray them and promised to fetch a locksmith to repair the lock. The servant gave them no encouragement, stating coldly that it would have been better not to touch something that belonged to his mistress.[1]

1. Walpole 1937–83, vol. 3 (1939), p. 62.

References: James Parker and Carl Christian Dauterman in Dauterman, Parker, and Standen 1964, pp. 144–49, no. 26, figs. 112–17; Baulez 1992, p. 53, ill. p. 52; Kisluk-Grosheide 2006, pp. 17–18, fig. 25.

30. Stand (*piètement*) for a model of La Samaritaine

Paris, 1773
Jean-Baptiste Vinceneux (ca. 1726–ca. 1795)
Carved, painted, gilded, and silvered walnut; modern wood top
H. 38⅛ in. (96.8 cm), w. 28¼ in. (71.7 cm), d. 22⅝ in. (57.4 cm)
Gift of Mr. and Mrs. Charles Wrightsman, 1983 (1983.185.7)

The hydraulic pump constructed on one of the piers of the Pont-Neuf was among the mechanical miracles of early seventeenth-century Paris. It supplied water from the river Seine to the fountains of the Louvre and Tuileries palaces. Between 1712 and 1719 the pump house was rebuilt by the well-known architect Robert de Cotte (1656–1735). Fitted with a carillon on its steep roof, the facade was adorned with a large clock and a sculptural group in lead representing Jesus and the Samarian woman at Jacob's Well. This group gave the new building its name: La Samaritaine.

In 1772 Charles-Philippe, comte d'Artois (1757–1836), ordered two maquettes of La Samaritaine, each with a removable roof, a clock on one side, a barometer on the other, and various luxury objects inside, such as a gold cadinet or casket to contain a set of cutlery and spices. Some thirty artists collaborated on this extraordinary commission, including the sculptor Louis-Simon Boizot (1743–1809), the clockmaker Robert Robin (1741–1799), and the bronze workers André Ravrio and Luc-Philippe Thomire, under the supervision of Pasquier, the *mécanicien* (engineer) to the comte d'Artois. One of these models was presented by the count to his sister-in-law, Marie-Antoinette, with whom he shared a close friendship. The other was for his bride-to-be, Marie-Thérèse of Savoy.

Fig. 41. Pasquier, model of the pump house known as La Samaritaine, 1772. Painted and gilded wood, gilt bronze, glass, and enamel. Clock movement by Robert Robin; barometer by Bourron. Musée Carnavalet, Paris (PM 034).

The Museum's stand, which has the crowned initials *MT* of the comtesse d'Artois, was executed by the little-known sculptor Jean-Baptiste Vinceneux for the model of La Samaritaine that belonged to her. Richly carved with oak, laurel, and myrtle branches, as well as with garlands of flowers, the stand displays a coat of arms on the back that has not yet been positively identified. A three-dimensional composition consisting of a classical urn, billing doves, a flaming torch, and a quiver of arrows adorns the cross-stretcher that connects the four slender legs. Symbolizing love and marital felicity, this group undoubtedly refers to the nuptials of the comte and comtesse d'Artois, which took place in November 1773, the same year the support was made; the marriage, however, proved an unhappy one as the young husband continued to lead a licentious life. Pierced guilloche moldings running along the sides of the stand allude to the fact that the models of La Samaritaine were intended to exude perfume. Placed on a later stand, one of the maquettes is in the collection of the Musée Carnavalet, Paris (fig. 41).

References: Watson 1966b, pp. 106–7, no. 72, ill.; Baulez and Ledoux-Lebard 1981, p. 10, fig. 8; Renée Davray-Piekolek in Gady and Pérouse de Montclos 2005, p. 338, under no. 84.

31. Combination table

Paris, ca. 1775
Martin Carlin (ca. 1730–1785)
Oak and pine veneered with tulipwood, sycamore, holly, boxwood, and ebony; Carrara marble; gilt-bronze mounts; accessories of Sèvres porcelain, rock crystal, silver gilt, and lacquer
Table h. 29 in. (73.6 cm), w. 27¾ in. (70.5 cm), d. 16⅜ in. (41.6 cm); bed table h. 9¼ in. (23.5 cm), w. 26⅞ in. (68.3 cm), d. 15½ in. (39.4 cm)
Gift of Mr. and Mrs. Charles Wrightsman, 1976 (1976.155.99a,b)

The principal occupation indeed of a French Lady is her Toilet.

—Elizabeth Seymour Percy, Duchess of Northumberland, diary entry for June 9, 1770

The daily ritual of dressing and grooming was taken very seriously in France, and it was not unusual for an aristocratic lady to receive visitors, who could even be called upon to assist her. Special pieces of furniture were designed for the toilette, such as this elegant marquetry table signed by Martin Carlin, which is more versatile than most dressing tables. The upper section can be removed to serve as a bed table, as it has its own short legs. It is fitted with an adjustable mirror that can be reversed to form a book rest (see detail below). A shallow drawer is provided in front, and the lidded compartments on either side are used for the storage of toilet articles. The lower section is a full-size table with a marble top, pull-out shelves in front and back, and drawers on both ends holding equipment for dressing, breakfasting, and writing. A trelliswork pattern enclosing rosettes, which may have been based on designs seen in Japanese lacquerwork,

Combination table with the upper section removed

embellishes the exterior of this multi-purpose piece, which is further enriched with gilt-bronze mounts.

Most dressing tables do not have as many fittings as the Museum's piece (not all of which are original), and for that reason it has been suggested that it was intended for use while traveling. However, the spindly legs are not provided with a threaded rod for detachment, meaning that the dressing table would have had to be transported intact. This makes it highly unlikely that the piece was meant to be taken on journeys, as it would not only prove cumbersome in the extreme but liable to damage en route. The table is a typical product of a *marchand-mercier*, who would have bought or ordered the various rock-crystal, Sèvres porcelain, and silver accoutrements and engaged a cabinet-maker to create the wooden frame. Martin Carlin, a German-born cabi-netmaker who had settled in Paris by 1759, specialized in making expensive and fashionable furniture and often collaborated with the dealers Simon-Philippe Poirier and Dominique Daguerre. A closely related combination table is in The Frick Collection, New York.

Epigraph. Northumberland 1752–74/1926, p. 135.

References: Watson 1966b, pp. 242–50, no. 124, ill.; Dauterman 1970, pp. 254–57, no. 105, ill.; Carl Christian Dauterman in Watson and Dauterman 1970, pp. 253–56, no. 68, ill.; Dell 1992, pp. 3–11 (mentioned on p. 8).

32. Drop-front secretary on stand (*secrétaire à abattant* or *secrétaire en cabinet*)

Paris, ca. 1776
Attributed to Martin Carlin (ca. 1730–1785);
central porcelain plaque painted by Edme-
François Bouillat the Elder (1739/40–1810)
Oak veneered with tulipwood, amaranth, holly,
and sycamore; six Sèvres soft-paste porcelain
plaques and two painted tin plaques; gilt-bronze
mounts; marble shelves; moiré silk
H. 43½ in. (110.5 cm), w. 40½ in. (102.9 cm),
d. 12⅞ in. (32.7 cm)
Gift of Mr. and Mrs. Charles Wrightsman, 1976
(1976.155.110)

Attributed to the cabinetmaker
Martin Carlin, who was known for
his graceful furniture mounted with
Sèvres porcelain, this exquisite two-
piece desk was made about 1776. A
date letter for that year is painted on
the back of the central porcelain
plaque, together with the mark of
Edme-François Bouillat (1739/40–
1810), a painter at the Sèvres manufactory. A specialist in different kinds
of floral ornament, Bouillat decorated
the main plaque with a flower basket
suspended from a large bowknot.

The history of this secretary is well
documented. During the eighteenth
century it graced the collections of
two remarkably different women. Its
first owner was the popular soprano
Marie-Joséphine Laguerre (1755–1783),
who as a *fille d'Opéra* enjoyed a luxurious and dissolute existence made
possible by her wealthy lovers. Her
personal property was publicly sold in
April 1782, less than a year before her
untimely death. The catalogue indicates that she owned this secretary as
well as two other pieces of furniture
embellished with porcelain plaques.
Some of the Sèvres decorative wares
in her collection may have been displayed on the marble shelves of the

secretary. It is likely that Dominique
Daguerre, who with his partner,
Simon-Philippe Poirier, had a virtual
monopoly on the purchase of Sèvres
plaques, supplied the piece of furniture to Laguerre and bought it back
at the 1782 sale, but this is not documented. In May of that same year,
Maria Feodorovna, grand duchess
of Russia, and her husband, Paul
(1754–1801), visited Paris incognito
as the comte and comtesse du Nord.
The future empress was described by
Jeanne-Louise-Henriette Campan
(1752–1822), first lady-in-waiting to
Marie-Antoinette, as being "of a fine
height, very fat for her age, with all
the stiffness of the German demean-
our."[1] In Paris, Maria Feodorovna
frequented the shops of the fashionable dealers, where she is likely to

have acquired the porcelain-mounted
secretary and other furnishings for
her country residence at Pavlovsk.
According to a detailed description of
her private rooms written in 1795 by
Maria Feodorovna herself, the secretary was placed in her boudoir.[2] It
remained at the imperial palace until
the Soviet government, which had
taken possession of Pavlovsk after the
Revolution of 1917, offered works of
art for sale to the dealer Joseph
Duveen (1869–1939), who had traveled to the Soviet Union in 1931.

1. Campan 1823, vol. 1, p. 237.
2. Feodorovna 1795/1903, p. 374.

References: Watson 1966b, pp. 186–90,
no. 105, ill.; Daniëlle O. Kisluk-Grosheide in
Kisluk-Grosheide, Koeppe, and Rieder 2006,
pp. 170–72, no. 71, ill.; Norberg 2007,
pp. 108–11, fig. 6.7.

33. Mechanical table (*table mécanique*)

Paris, 1778
Jean-Henri Riesener (1734–1806); mechanism
by Jean-Gotfritt Mercklein (1733–1808)
Oak veneered with marquetry of *bois satiné*,
holly, amaranth, barberry, stained sycamore,
and green-lacquered wood; gilt-bronze mounts;
steel, iron, and brass fittings; mirror glass; velvet
(not original)
H. 31 in. (78.7 cm), w. 44½ in. (113 cm),
d. 27¼ in. (69.2 cm)
Rogers Fund, 1933 (33.12)

The number 2964 painted underneath the top of this table corresponds to an entry in the *Journal du Garde-Meuble de la Couronne* (a ledger listing new furniture for the royal residences) and identifies this multipurpose table as one of the first pieces ordered by Marie-Antoinette from her favorite cabinetmaker, Jean-Henri Riesener. A native of Westphalia, Riesener had a successful career in Paris and made many sumptuous pieces for the queen. This table was delivered to Versailles on December 12, 1778, exactly a week before the long-awaited birth of her first child, Marie-Thérèse-Charlotte. To alleviate Marie-Antoinette's discomfort during the advanced state of her pregnancy, this table was fitted by Mercklein, a *mécanicien* in her service, with a special mechanism. Hidden behind a finely decorated gilt-bronze plaque at either end, this mechanism allowed the queen to use the table in either a seated or a standing position. By means of a detachable crank at one side, the top can be raised or lowered on ratcheted metal shafts that move up or down in the hollow legs (see detail below). The table could be used for various activities such as eating and writing and also reading and dressing, since the central panel of the top can be lifted to form a lectern and reversed to reveal a mirror. Pressing buttons along the front edge of the table releases the hinged lids to six compartments for the storage of cosmetic and writing equipment. The intricate marquetry decoration of the top has lost some of its subtle coloring over time. Framed alternately with natural (originally white) holly and black-stained holly, the *bois satiné* trelliswork encloses rosettes cut of an originally bright yellow barberry wood against a stained, soft yellow sycamore ground.

References: Verlet 1994, pp. 158–61, no. 17, ill.; Kisluk-Grosheide 2006, pp. 20, 22, figs. 27, 28; William Rieder in Kisluk-Grosheide, Koeppe, and Rieder 2006, pp. 176–77, no. 73, ill.

Detail showing the crank

34. Armchair
(*fauteuil à la reine*)

Paris, 1779
Designed by Jacques Gondouin (1737–1818);
made by François II Foliot (1748–?1839);
carved by the workshop of Madame Pierre-
Edme Babel; gilded by the workshop of Marie-
Catherine Renon
Carved and gilded beech; modern silk lampas
H. 39 in. (99.1 cm), w. 25½ in. (64.8 cm),
d. 19¾ in. (50.2 cm)
Gift of Susan Dwight Bliss, 1944 (44.157.2)

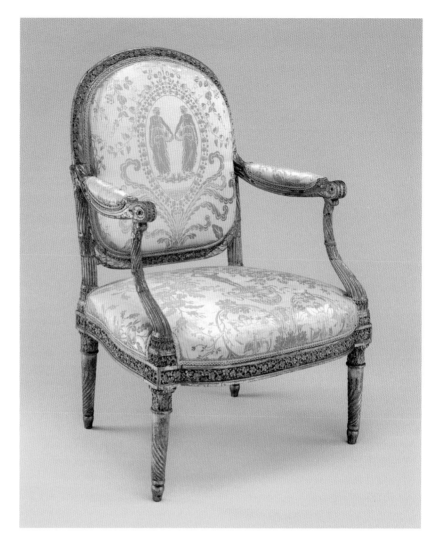

After the American diplomat Gouverneur Morris (1752–1816) visited the Château de Versailles on March 21, 1789, he wrote in his diary: "The Queen's Apartments I cannot see because her Majesty is there, and yet 'tis ten to one but I should like her better than any other Part of the Furniture."[1] Nevertheless, during the Revolutionary sales of 1793 and 1794 Morris purchased a set of seat furniture, including this armchair, that had belonged to Marie-Antoinette. He had the pieces shipped to his family home, Morrisania, a country estate north of New York City.

During the twentieth century, some confusion arose regarding the early provenance of the armchair. In 1920, when in the collection of Mrs. George T. Bliss, it was called "the Lafayette chair," though the marquis de Lafayette (1757–1834), who fought in America under George Washington during the Revolutionary War, had in all probability never seen or sat in it.[2] When Mrs. Bliss's daughter, Susan Dwight Bliss, gave it to the Museum in 1944, family tradition held that it had once been in the possession of Thomas Jefferson (1743–1826), who served as minister to France from 1785 to 1789 and later became the third president of the United States.

The armchair was commissioned in 1779 for use during the winter in Marie-Antoinette's Grand Cabinet Intérieur at the palace, and the crowned double *V* for "Versailles" on the webbing underneath the seat bears witness to its royal provenance. The architect Jacques Gondouin designed not only the seat furniture but also the lavish silk-satin brocade that was to line the walls of the room and used to upholster the furniture. François II Foliot, member of an important family of Parisian chair-makers, or *menuisiers*, fashioned the chair's frame and assembled it. The finished chair was the product of a true collaboration by members of various guilds, as is attested by bills that reveal the names of the different artists and craftsmen involved. The dense floral borders of the seat and back rails, the inverted cornucopias serving as arm supports, and the legs fluted in spirals and surmounted by leaf capitals were carved in the work-shop of Madame Pierre-Edme Babel. Marie-Catherine Renon, who continued the workshop of her late husband, Gaspard-Marie Bardou, charged for the gilding of the chair, which was upholstered by Claude-François Capin.

The chair and other pieces of the set did not stay long in the queen's Grand Cabinet Intérieur at Versailles. They were removed in 1783, when she had the room redecorated with white and gold paneling, and they were later used in a small upstairs room.

1. Morris 1789–93/1939, vol. 1, p. 16.
2. The architect Louis Metcalf to Mrs. George T. Bliss, August 18, 1920, Bliss Family Papers, 1842–1961, Manuscripts and Archives Division, New York Public Library.

References: Verlet 1994, pp. 210–18, 263, no. 30, ill.; Kisluk-Grosheide 2006, pp. 22–24, figs. 29, 30; Daniëlle O. Kisluk-Grosheide in Kisluk-Grosheide, Koeppe, and Rieder 2006, pp. 178–80, no. 74, ill.

35. Pair of armchairs (*fauteuils à la reine*)

Paris, ca. 1780–85
Georges Jacob (1739–1814)
Carved and gilded walnut; embroidered silk satin
H. 40¼ in. (102.2 cm), w. 29½ in. (74.9 cm), d. 30⅝ in. (77.8 cm)
Gift of Samuel H. Kress Foundation, 1958 (58.75.25, 26)

Part of a set of seat furniture, this armchair was in the possession of Louis-Jean-Marie de Bourbon, duc de Penthièvre (1725–1793), grand admiral of France and a cousin of Louis XVI. Marks underneath the frame indicate that the chair was made by Georges Jacob for the ceremonial bedchamber at the duke's Parisian residence, the Hôtel de Toulouse. As *fauteuils meublants*, the

armchairs of the set would have been placed in a formal arrangement along the walls of the room. The smaller side chairs would have formed a second row around the center of the room.

This chair is among the few pieces of seat furniture in the Museum's collection that have kept both their original show covers and their under-upholstery. The removable back panel, arm pads, seat cushion, and edge roll below are upholstered with silk satin that is embellished with chain-stitched embroidery of high quality. The duke seems to have been

very fond of such polychrome needle-work on a light ground, as is documented by the large bills he received from the workshops of two *brodeurs*—Baudouin, possibly Joseph-François-Xavier Baudouin (1739–ca. 1786), and the not yet identified Boucher—for embroidered hangings and upholstery they created for the Châteaux de Sceaux and de Bizy between 1775 and 1780.[1] Could the same workshops also have been responsible for the once very colorful floral needlework on the Museum's armchair? It includes certain motifs in the border—such as the string of pearls with foliage winding around it—that harmonize with the carving of the walnut frame (see detail page 93). Especially noteworthy in this respect are the deeply undercut myrtle branches spiraling around a straight rod on the seat and back rails, which must have been very difficult to achieve. Trails of berried myrtle coil around the tapering legs, which are crowned by collars of laurel leaves. Branches of both these evergreen shrubs not only embellished eighteenth-century furniture, porcelain, and other decorative objects but were also present in the French interior in a different form. Mixed with dried flower petals, herbs, and spices, their fragrant leaves were used as ingredients of potpourri.

1. See Serrette 2009, pp. 64–65.

References: James Parker in Dauterman, Parker, and Standen 1964, pp. 61–66, no. 7a–d, ill.; Daniëlle O. Kisluk-Grosheide in Kisluk-Grosheide, Koeppe, and Rieder 2006, pp. 189–92, no. 78, ill.

36. Mechanical gaming table

Neuwied, Germany, ca. 1780–83
David Roentgen (1743–1807)
Oak and walnut veneered with mahogany, holly and stained holly, and maple and stained maple; iron, steel, and brass fittings; felt; leather
H. 30⅞ in. (78.4 cm), w. 38¾ in. (98.3 cm), d. 19½ in. (49.5 cm)
Pfeiffer Fund, 2007 (2007.42.1a–e)

An advertisement in the periodical *Annonces, affiches et avis divers* for January 8, 1781, listed the furniture for sale in the Parisian shop of David Roentgen. Among the various pieces mentioned were tables for playing quadrille, trictrac, and other games, executed in mahogany and well finished and polished like marble, a description that would fit an ingeniously crafted table like this one in the Museum's collection. Fitted with a triple top, the multifunctional piece can be converted from a console table (when closed) to a felt-covered card- or game table with an inlaid checkered surface for chess and to a leather-lined desk for reading and writing, complete with a ratcheted book rest. Furthermore, it harbors a box rising on springs with a backgammon board that can be taken out for separate use. The table also includes two tambour-covered compartments for the storage of cards, counters, and other paraphernalia. One of the back supports has a gateleg mechanism that can be adjusted to hold the hinged leaves at different angles. With the attention to detail typical of Roentgen's Neuwied workshop—one of the most productive and successful in Europe—the surfaces of the Museum's table were veneered with figured mahogany resembling veined marble.

Born and active in the Rhineland, the enterprising Roentgen sold furniture all over Europe, including Versailles. In 1780 he became a mem-

36

ber of the Parisian guild of cabinet-makers, and the following year he opened his own store in the French capital. Roentgen rarely signed his pieces, and although this table is typical of his output it bears the stamp of the French cabinetmaker Pierre

Macret (1727–ca. 1796). Macret stopped making furniture in 1771; however, he may have repaired or sold this multifunctional table (and stamped it at that time) before retiring from business in 1787. Macret's stamp indicates that this sophisticated piece of

Neoclassical furniture was in Paris during the eighteenth century and may, in fact, have been made specifically for the French market.

References: Fabian 1996, pp. 56–57, no. 85, ill.; Wolfram Koeppe in "Recent Acquisitions" 2007, p. 34, ill.

37. Mechanical table (*table mécanique*)

Paris, 1781
Jean-Henri Riesener (1734–1806)
Oak veneered with *bois satiné*, amaranth, holly,
barberry, and various stained marquetry woods;
gilt-bronze mounts; iron and brass fittings;
mirror glass; velvet (not original)
H. 28½ in. (72.4 cm), w. 30¾ in. (78.1 cm),
d. 19 in. (48.3 cm)
The Jules Bache Collection, 1949 (49.7.117)

Described in an inventory of 1789
simply as a writing table, this wonderful piece offered its original
owner, Marie-Antoinette, many more
options than that. Made by Jean-
Henri Riesener in 1781 for the queen's
Grand Cabinet Intérieur at Versailles,
the table is fitted with a mechanism
that allows the top to slide back and,
at the same time, the main drawer to
move forward. The central compartment of the drawer encloses a velvet-
lined writing surface that can be
ratcheted up to form a bookstand and
reversed to show a mirror. The marquetry surface on top is richly embellished with a pattern of trelliswork
enclosing rosettes frequently used by
Riesener on furniture for Marie-
Antoinette. The central medallion
encloses a trophy with the attributes
of Poetry and Literature and the Latin
motto *Numine afflatur* ("inspired by
the divine nod"). This exquisite
marquetry decoration, now faded,
must originally have confirmed an
eighteenth-century description of the
technique as "painting in wood."
Judging from the well-preserved
marquetry on the lids of the inner
compartments, which can be released
by pressing a small button on the
drawer front, and on the outer sides of
the drawers, visible when the table is

open, the exquisite design of the top must have been very colorful. This the cabinetmaker achieved through a clever selection of contrasting woods and the use of organic and, therefore, not very permanent dyes to expand the natural palette of the wood. The table is mounted with gilt-bronze moldings around the top, along the lower edge of the frieze, and running down the tapering legs. Gilt-bronze plaques in relief adorn the drawer front and the sides. This multifunctional *table mécanique* was sent to the Château de Saint-Cloud in 1785, where it was placed in Marie-Antoinette's dressing room and later used there with a daybed, *bergère*, and fire screen by Jean-Baptiste-Claude Sené, now also at the Museum (nos. 49–51).

References: Verlet 1994, pp. 166–69, no. 19, ill.; Kisluk-Grosheide 2006, p. 24, figs. 32, 33; William Rieder in Kisluk-Grosheide, Koeppe, and Rieder 2006, pp. 187–89, no. 77, ill.

38. Tester bed (*lit à la duchesse en impériale*)

Paris, ca. 1782–83
Georges Jacob (1739–1814)
Carved, painted, and gilded walnut, pine, and linden; iron hardware; silk and wool Beauvais tapestry; modern silk damask
Headboard h. 79 in. (200.7 cm), w. 73½ in. (186.7 cm); bedstead l. 86¼ in. (220.35 cm); tester w. 84½ in. (214.6 cm), l. 96¾ in. (245.7 cm)
Gift of Kingdon Gould, in memory of his mother, Edith Kingdon Gould, 1923 (23.235a,d)

As its full-size domed canopy is suspended from the ceiling rather than supported on posts, this tester bed, which bears the stamp of the *menuisier* Georges Jacob, is a type called *lit à la duchesse en impériale*. Its original but now fragile hangings, woven in 1782–83 at the Beauvais tapestry manufactory after designs by Jean-Baptiste Huet (1745–1811), have been replaced by modern silk damask, except for the lining of the interior dome. French eighteenth-century beds tended to be lofty, as it was cus-

tomary to pile them with three or more mattresses filled with straw, wool, horsehair, or feathers. Tobias Smollett (1721–1771) noted in 1766, "French beds are so high, that sometimes one is obliged to mount them by the help of steps."[1]

The custom of receiving visitors while reposing in a large and elegantly fitted out bed was practiced in France during the eighteenth century mostly by aristocratic women. The Museum's imposing piece of furniture with its exquisitely carved floral decoration, the work of an unknown carver, must have formed a splendid backdrop for such official calls or congratulatory visits. In 1791 the bed is documented as standing in the large bedchamber of Guyonne-Marguerite de Durfort de Lorge, duchesse de Choiseul-Praslin (1737–1806), at her Parisian home, the Hôtel de Belle Isle. Following the turmoil of the Revolution and the

political changes of the early nineteenth century, the bed was sold in Paris in 1830. It became part of the famous collections at Hamilton Palace, South Lanarkshire, Scotland, the residence of Alexander Hamilton Douglas, tenth Duke of Hamilton (1767–1852), where it was placed in one of the state rooms. The duke's grandson sold the contents of the palace, including the bed, at a highly anticipated auction that took place in 1882. Through the intermediation of several dealers, the bed was acquired in 1897 by the financier and railroad executive George J. Gould (1864–1923). His wife, the former actress Edith M. Kingdon (1864–1921), used it in her bedroom of their New York town house.

1. Smollett 1766/1969, p. 43.

References: Remington 1924, ill.; Standen 1985, vol. 2, pp. 564–67, no. 84, ill.; Kisluk-Grosheide 2009, figs. 1–4, 8, 9, 20, 22.

39, 40. Commode and drop-front secretary (*secrétaire à abattant* or *secrétaire en armoire*)

Paris, 1783
Jean-Henri Riesener (1734–1806)
Oak veneered with ebony and 17th-century
Japanese lacquer; interiors veneered with tulipwood, amaranth, holly, and ebonized holly;
gilt-bronze mounts; marble; velvet (not original)
Commode h. 36¾ in. (93.4 cm), w. 56½ in.
(143.5 cm), d. 23½ in. (59.7 cm); secretary
h. 57 in. (144.8 cm), w. 43 in. (109.2 cm), d. 16 in.
(40.6 cm)
Bequest of William K. Vanderbilt, 1920
(20.155.12, 11)

Jean-Henri Riesener created this splendid secretary and commode for Marie-Antoinette in 1783. They were commissioned for the queen's Grand Cabinet Intérieur at Versailles, where she kept the collection of Japanese lacquer boxes she had inherited from her mother, Empress Maria Theresa (1717–1780) of Austria. So that their surface decoration would harmonize with that of the boxes, choice fragments of seventeenth-century Japanese lacquer were reused as veneer for these pieces of royal furniture. The shiny black and gold lacquer and lustrous ebony form a striking background for the exceptionally beautiful gilt-bronze mounts (see detail page 102). Consisting of swags and interlaced garlands of naturalistic flowers, these jewel-like mounts incorporate the queen's initials in the frieze as well as handles shaped like rippling ribbons.

Enclosed behind the fall front of the secretary, several secret drawers are hidden beneath the hinged floor of the central compartment. These small drawers, as well as a strongbox that could be locked separately, offered places to store valuables and protect personal correspondence from prying eyes. The queen undoubtedly used them, for she never believed any papers were safe at the court, according to the Austrian diplomat Florimond-Claude, comte de Mercy-Argenteau (1727–1794). He had reported to her mother many years earlier that the dauphine was fearful of duplicate keys and apprehensive that things would

39

Left front corner of the secretary

41. Pair of side chairs (*chaises à la reine*)

Paris, 1784
Made by Georges Jacob (1739–1814); carved by
Jules-Hugues Rousseau (1743–1806) and Jean-
Siméon Rousseau de la Rottière (1747–1820);
gilded by Presle
Carved and gilded walnut; silk moiré damask
(not original)
H. 34 in. (86.4 cm), w. 18½ in. (47 cm), d. 18 in.
(45.7 cm)
Gift of Mr. and Mrs. Charles Wrightsman, 1977
(1977.102.13, 14)

be taken from her pockets at night.[1]

The history of these famous pieces of furniture is remarkably well documented. Marie-Antoinette frequently changed the decor of her private rooms, and in 1787 she had the commode and secretary sent from Versailles to her new summer palace at Saint-Cloud. Both pieces left the royal collections when they were given in lieu of payment for his services during the Revolution to Abraham Alcan, a contractor of supplies for the army of the Rhine and Moselle. During the nineteenth century, the queen's secretary and commode were part of several notable British collections. George Watson Taylor (1770–1841) kept them at his country house, Erlestoke Park, in Wiltshire, and later they belonged to the dukes of Hamilton. At the famous Hamilton Palace sale of 1882 the royal pieces were acquired for Mrs. William Kissam Vanderbilt (1853–1933), one of the reigning society hostesses of New York City, for her mansion on Fifth Avenue. Her daughter Consuelo Vanderbilt Balsan (1877–1964) remembered Marie-Antoinette's lacquer *secrétaire* and commode standing in the white drawing room, which was hung with a set of Boucher tapestries.[2]

1. Mercy-Argenteau 1770–80/1874, vol. 1, p. 75.
2. Balsan 1952, p. 11.

References: Baulez 1985, p. 151; Verlet 1994, pp. 201–7, no. 28, ill.; Baulez 2001, pp. 30, 32–34, figs. 5, 6; Rieder 2002, figs. 1–8; Kisluk-Grosheide 2006, pp. 24, 26–27, figs. 34–37; William Rieder in Kisluk-Grosheide, Koeppe, and Rieder 2006, pp. 198–201, nos. 82, 83, ill.

"At eleven o'clock set out for the Thuilleries, to see the balloon go off; we soon quitted the coach, and it was with the greatest difficulty we got through the crowd on the Pont-royal to the little garden door. It was not long afterwards, that the Duke of Cumberland was in danger of being squeezed to death, as announced in all the public journals. The Queen of France sat in the balcony in front of the Thuilleries, appeared serious, and our party remarked, that she looked like a very handsome English woman. As soon as the aëronauts had taken their flight, I quitted the gardens."[1] In his diary entry for December 1, 1783, Joseph Cradock (1742–1826) refers to the many spectators who watched a historic event take place that day: the first manned hydrogen balloon flight. The aeronauts Jacques-Alexandre-César Charles (1746–1823), a physicist, and his collaborator, Marie-Noël Robert (1760–1820), took off from the gardens of the Tuileries in a gondola suspended from a netted hydrogen balloon (see fig. 42).

Balloon-shaped and carved with netting, the finials of these side chairs, supplied for the queen's boudoir at the

Château des Tuileries in February 1784, celebrate Charles and Robert's successful flight. Georges Jacob, one of the outstanding *menuisiers* of the ancien régime, provided the walnut frames, which he described as "of a new shape," possibly referring to the arched top rail or the seat shaped like a horseshoe. The brothers Rousseau, who were decorative painters as well as sculptors, executed the delicate carving, each element of which is carefully detailed in their 1784 invoice. The chairs' legs have the form of arrow-filled quivers, and the uprights of the back are shaped like fasces, or bundles of rods tied with ribbon, which symbolized power or authority in classical antiquity. The now little-known Presle, who advertised as "painter and gilder to the king," gilded the frames. For certain details of the carving, such as the myrtle branches on the seat rails, a clear greenish tone of gilding was chosen to subtly contrast with the yellow gold used elsewhere.

1. Cradock 1828, vol. 2, pp. 38–39.

References: Watson 1966b, pp. 50–51, no. 36a, b, ill.; Kisluk-Grosheide 2006, pp. 44–46, figs. 68, 69; Daniëlle O. Kisluk-Grosheide in Kisluk-Grosheide, Koeppe, and Rieder 2006, pp. 202–4, no. 84, ill.

Fig. 42. Louis-Alexandre Boutelou, after a design by Duperreux, *Balloon Built by MM Charles and Robert, as It Rose from the Tuileries Garden on December 1, 1783*, ca. 1783. Engraving. U.S. Air Force Academy Library, Colorado, Gimbel Collection of Aeronautical History (XL-4-1125).

Detail of chair back with finial

42. *Still Life with an Allegory of Motherly Love*

Rome, 1784
Aubert-Henri-Joseph Parent (1753–1835)
Lime wood
H. 27¾ in. (70.5 cm), w. 20⅝ in. (52.4 cm)
Gift of Mr. and Mrs. Charles Wrightsman, 1971
(1971.206.39)

Carved of a single piece of soft lime wood, this high relief with its daring undercutting is an excellent example of the virtuoso work for which the French sculptor Aubert Parent was justly known. Reminiscent of Dutch seventeenth-century flower paintings, Parent's still lifes then as now drew admiration for their realism, delicacy, and the remarkable liveliness of the birds and other small creatures that inhabit them. The inscription below—AUBERT PARENT. EQUES RO. INV. SCULP. ROMA AN. 1784—indicates that this panel was created in Rome in 1784, the year that the artist, supported by a royal stipend, traveled to Italy.

The classical vocabulary that Parent mastered there is reflected in the shape and decoration of the urn filled with tulips, roses, lilacs, lilies-of-the-valley, and other sweet-scented blooms. A grapevine harboring a linnet's nest surrounds the base, and while one bird feeds the fledglings its mate brings additional food. The artist's predilection for symbols of motherly love and domestic life is reflected in the nesting birds and in the low relief on the plinth of a woman with her offspring, one of them a suckling infant. These themes had been made fashionable by Jean-Jacques Rousseau's philosophical treatise

Émile, of 1762, which extols the benefits of nursing one's own children. The body of the vase is appropriately adorned with the bearded mask of the celestial god Jupiter, also known as protector of family life.

Reference: Streeter 1985, p. 63, fig. 6.

43. Armchair
(fauteuil à la reine)

Paris, ca. 1785
Attributed to Georges Jacob (1739–1814)
Carved and gilded beech; silk upholstery (not original)
H. 38¾ in. (98.4 cm), w. 26⅜ in. (67 cm), d. 23⅝ in. (60 cm)
Gift of J. Pierpont Morgan, 1907 (07.225.106)

This armchair with a medallion-shaped back surmounted by a rippled bowknot, its columnar uprights surmounted by finials shaped like flaming cassolettes, seems to be depicted in two paintings by Adélaïde Labille-Guiard (1749–1803). Principal painter to "Mesdames Tantes," the unmarried aunts of Louis XVI, Labille-Guiard exhibited a full-length portrait of Madame Adélaïde at the Salon of 1787 (fig. 43). The princess stands in front of the chair, her robe draped over its arm. Three years later the artist painted Charles-Roger, prince de Bauffremont (1713–1795), seated in what seems to be the same chair. In both portraits it is upholstered in blue-green velvet. Since no other armchair of this model is known, it is possible that this very piece of seat furniture once belonged to Madame Adélaïde. According to Éléonore-Charlotte-Adélaïde-Louise d'Osmond, comtesse de Boigne (1781–1866), whose mother had been a lady-in-waiting to the princess, she was considered the cleverest of the Mesdames Tantes. She hated wine and strongly objected to the common habit of spitting, becoming enraged if anyone spat in her presence. She never married, preferring to keep her position as a Daughter of France.[1] Together with her sister Victoire, Madame Adélaïde ordered fashionable furnishings for the Château de Bellevue, their country residence overlooking the Seine, which had formerly belonged to Madame de Pompadour.

1. Boigne 1781–1830/1907–8, vol. 1, pp. 44–45.

References: Pératé and Brière 1908, vol. 3, pp. 28–29, pl. CXI; Parker 1966, pp. 188–91, fig. 9.

Fig. 43. Adélaïde Labille-Guiard, *Madame Adélaïde, Daughter of Louis XV*, 1787. Oil on canvas. Versailles, Musée National des Châteaux de Versailles et de Trianon (inv. MV3958).

44. Fire screen (*écran*)

Paris, ca. 1786
Georges Jacob (1739–1814)
Carved, gilded, and silvered beech; 18th-century
silk brocade (not original)
H. 42 in. (106.7 cm), w. 26¾ in. (67.9 cm), d. of
base 16¼ in. (41.3 cm)
Gift of Mr. and Mrs. Charles Wrightsman, 1971
(1971.206.16)

On a visit to the royal palace of Fontainebleau on September 14, 1787, Arthur Young described Marie-Antoinette's then recently redecorated boudoir as a delicious little room with exquisite painting, observing that "nothing can exceed the extremity of ornament that is here with taste bestowed."[1] Designed by the architect Pierre Rousseau (1751–1829), the queen's boudoir at Fontainebleau is, indeed, a jewel box of a room. Its large mirrors alternate with shimmering mother-of-pearl-like *boiserie* painted by Michel-Hubert Bourgeois and his assistant Jacques-Louis-François Touzé with light-hearted arabesques and flowers. An important aspect of the interior decoration was the matching seat furniture supplied by Georges Jacob and clearly intended to harmonize with the gold and silver tones of the decor. This screen's gilded frame incorporates silvered highlights, now much worn, such as the wisps of ivy trailing around the uprights shaped like burning torches. The overall unity in the design of the room and its furnishings was also expressed through the subtle repetition of certain decorative motifs. The cupid's bow and wreath of roses, symbols of love, carved on top of the fire screen, for instance, recur in gilt bronze on the mantelpiece, where they are combined with ivy. The motif of a string of pearls pulled through a spiraling ribbon is used not only to embellish the screen (see detail below) but to frame the wall paneling of the room as well.

1. Young 1792, pp. 55–56.

References: Carlier 2006, pp. 38–47, fig. 35; Kisluk-Grosheide 2006, p. 44, figs. 65, 66.

Detail of one of the uprights with finial

45. Drop-front secretary (*secrétaire à abattant* or *secrétaire en armoire*)

Paris, 1786–87
Guillaume Benneman (d. 1811)
Oak veneered with tulipwood, kingwood, holly
partly stained green, ebony, and mahogany;
brèche d'Alep marble (not original); modern
leather
H. 63½ in. (161.3 cm), w. 32 in. (81.3 cm),
d. 15 in. (38.1 cm)
Mounts: modeled by Louis-Simon Boizot
(1743–1809), Gilles-François (?) Martin
(ca. 1713–1795), and Michaud; probably cast by
Étienne-Jean or Pierre-Auguste Forestier;
chased by Pierre-Philippe Thomire (1751–1843),
Badin, Tournay, and others; gilded by Galle
Gilt bronze
Gift of Mr. and Mrs. Charles Wrightsman, 1971
(1971.206.17)

This unusually well documented
secretary—known as a *secrétaire en
armoire* because the section below the
drop front, or *abattant*, is fitted as a
cupboard (*armoire*)—beautifully
illustrates the collaborative nature of
high-quality furniture production in
eighteenth-century France. Because of
strict guild regulations that enforced
high standards of workmanship and
stimulated a high degree of specialization, many different artists were
involved in its creation. Intended for
Louis XVI's study at the Château de
Compiègne, a palatial hunting lodge
fifty miles northeast of Paris, this piece
was ordered to match an existing commode made by Gilles Joubert for
Louis XV in 1770. Jean Hauré
(b. 1739), a sculptor and *entrepreneur
des meubles* to the court, supervised the
work and engaged the German-born
Guillaume Benneman, who had been
named king's cabinetmaker in 1785, to
execute the frame and the marquetry.
The curvilinear latticework pattern of
the marquetry was originally enriched
with small gilded rosettes. The gilt-

bronze mounts went through the hands
of many different artists and craftsmen
(listed above) during successive modeling, casting, chasing, burnishing,
and mercury-gilding procedures.
Jean-Pierre Lanfant supplied the
original top of dark red Italian griotte
marble, which has since been replaced.
The detailed receipts for the work also
record payments for leather to cover
the writing surface and for the gilt
tooling of its edges, as well as for the
services of a locksmith. Although this

secretary was supposed to match a
nearly twenty-year-old commode, the
mounts, especially the large caryatids—veritable sculptures in their own
right—and the interior—veneered
with mahogany—are expressions of
the latest Neoclassical taste.

References: Watson 1966b, pp. 195–201,
no. 107, ill.; Verlet 1994, pp. 197–200, 262,
no. 27, ill.; Kisluk-Grosheide 2006, pp. 37–38,
40, figs. 60, 61; Wolfram Koeppe in Kisluk-
Grosheide, Koeppe, and Rieder 2006,
pp. 204–7, no. 85, ill.

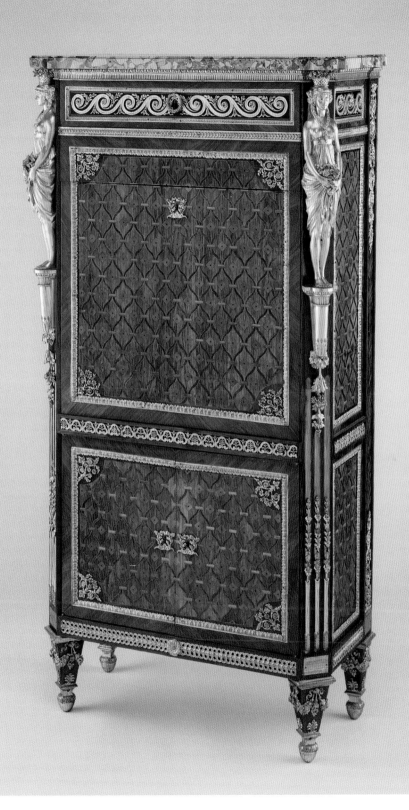

46. Three side chairs (*chaises à la reine*)

Paris, 1786–87
Made by Jean-Baptiste Boulard (ca. 1725–1789);
carved by Nicolas-François Vallois (1738–1788)
or Lambert Charny (active 1756–86), under the
direction of Jean Hauré (b. 1739); gilded by
Louis-François Chatard (ca. 1749–1819), Julliac,
or Guintrange
Carved and gilded beech; silk damask (not
original)
H. 36½ in. (92.8 cm), w. 22½ in. (57.1 cm),
d. 19¾ in. (50.2 cm)
Fletcher Fund, 1945 (45.60.44–46)

Various games of cards and chance, such as lansquenet, faro, quadrille, piquet, and cavagnole, had long been popular entertainment at the French court, where the stakes were high and entire fortunes could be won or lost at the gaming table. Reporting to Empress Maria Theresa on March 18, 1777, the Austrian diplomat Florimond-Claude de Mercy-Argenteau declared: "The gambling of the Queen grows more and more unrestrained. The public know that the identical games, strictly prohibited to them by the laws of Paris, are played nightly and to excess by the Queen."[1] To accommodate all those who might wish to participate in the play, a large set of furniture consisting of thirty side chairs, six *voyeuses*, or spectators' chairs, and a fire screen was ordered on August 12, 1786, for Louis XVI's Salon des Jeux (Gaming Room) at the Château de Fontainebleau. A label pasted underneath the seats of the Museum's three chairs identifies them as part of this ensemble, which was commissioned for the court's annual sojourn at Fontainebleau in October 1787. The set was never used as intended because the royal visit did not occur that year or the next. In fact, the king and his family left Versailles in October 1789, never to return to the palace, nor did they visit Fontainebleau again.

The various *mémoires* documenting the creation of the seat furniture illustrate the typical eighteenth-century division of labor in such projects. The *menuisier* Boulard, who received many commissions from the court, cut the wood for the chairs with their arched top rail and slightly curving seat rails and assembled them. The decorative carving, consisting of guilloche and pearl motifs matching the ornament of the door cases in the king's Salon des Jeux, was done under the direction of Jean Hauré by the sculptors Nicolas-François Vallois and Lambert Charny, who were responsible for, respectively, twenty-four and twelve chairs each. Three different gilders were called upon to finish the frames, and the upholsterer Claude-François Capin (d. 1789) covered the set in blue, white, and gray lampas with an arabesque design woven for this purpose by the firm of Louis Reboul, Fontebrune et Cie in Lyons. The seat rails of the Museum's chairs are slightly lower than those on some of the other side chairs of this suite, indicating that they were among the twelve intended to have a removable seat cushion.

1. Quoted in Smythe 1770–80/1902, vol. 2, pp. 481–82; see also Mercy-Argenteau 1770–80/1874, vol. 3, p. 35.

References: Verlet 1994, pp. 226–28, 264, no. 34, ill.; other chairs of this set discussed by: Pallot 1993, pp. 154–55, no. 54; Hughes 1996, vol. 1, pp. 185–90, no. 34 (mentioned p. 190); Condamy 2008, pp. 263–66 (mentioned p. 264).

47. Drop-front secretary on stand (*secrétaire à abattant* or *secrétaire en cabinet*)

Paris, ca. 1787
Attributed to Adam Weisweiler (1744–1820);
some mounts by François Rémond (1747–1812);
Sèvres plaque decorated about 1782 by Edme-
François Bouillat the Elder (1739/40–1810),
its borders attributed to Geneviève Tallandier
(active 1774–98)
Oak veneered with burl thuja, amaranth,
mahogany, satinwood, holly, and ebonized holly;
painted metal; one Sèvres soft-paste porcelain
plaque; fifteen Wedgwood jasper medallions;
gilt-bronze mounts; marble; leather (not original)
H. 51 in. (129.5 cm), w. 27 in. (68.6 cm), d. 16 in.
(40.6 cm)
Gift of Samuel H. Kress Foundation, 1958
(58.75.57)

After an angry mob stormed the palace of Versailles during the night of October 5–6, 1789, Gouverneur Morris recorded in his diary that "Many Circumstances of Insult to the royal Personages" had occurred. "The Queen obliged to fly from her Bed in her Shift and Petticoat with her Stockings in her Hand to the King's Chamber for Protection, being pursued by the *Poissardes* [fishwives]."[1] Following this shocking incident, the royal family was forced to return to Paris, where they lived for three years under house arrest in the Château des Tuileries. A few days after their arrival, the queen consigned to the dealer Dominique Daguerre and his partner, Martin-Eloi Lignereux (1750–1809), a number of her most treasured possessions for safekeeping. Among those objects was a porcelain-mounted secretary, which may, in

fact, have been this one and possibly was the last piece of furniture Daguerre had delivered to Marie-Antoinette for use at Versailles. Nevertheless, in 1794 an inventory of the seized royal furniture stored at the palace was drawn up by the new regime, and among the pieces listed was a secretary, its drop front mounted with a large Sèvres plaque and ten medallions forming garlands—a description that seems to fit the Museum's piece. It was among the former royal objects that Abraham Alcan, the leading military contractor, selected as payment for his services during the Revolution. During the nineteenth century Charles Mills (1792–1872), a London banker and art collector with a taste for Sèvres porcelain and furniture mounted with Sèvres plaques, acquired this secretary. His collection remained intact until the 1930s, when the Lords Hillingdon, descendants of Mills, sold it to the well-known art dealer Joseph Duveen, who in turn offered it with a group of artworks from the Hillingdon collection to the businessman and philanthropist Samuel H. Kress (1863–1955).

The interlaced stretchers and bulbous, downward-tapering legs of this graceful secretary are characteristic of the work of Adam Weisweiler; moreover, the gilt-bronze female half-figures used as corner mounts

appear on other pieces by this cabinetmaker. Born in the Rhineland, Weisweiler settled in Paris in the late 1770s, and there he is known to have worked for Daguerre. Edme-François Bouillat the Elder, one of the most talented flower painters at Sèvres, was responsible for the ribbon-tied bouquet on the central plaque. According to a label pasted on the back, the price was 336 livres, and we know that Daguerre purchased a plaque for that amount in 1782. The *pointillé* (stippled) borders are attributed to Madame Vincent Tallandier, who with her husband specialized in this kind of decoration. Framed in gilt-bronze garlands that lend them a jewel-like quality, fifteen Wedgwood jasperware cameos decorate the front and sides of the desk. Some show classical scenes based on antique gems. Others depict mothers and children engaged in domestic pursuits. They formed part of a so-called Domestic Employment series first advertised in a Wedgwood catalogue of 1787, which suggests a date for the secretary, as does the fact that in the same year Daguerre signed an agreement with Josiah Wedgwood (1730–1795) to sell his wares in Paris.

1. Morris 1789–93/1939, vol. 1, p. 245.

References: James Parker and Carl Christian Dauterman in Dauterman, Parker, and Standen 1964, pp. 154–61, no. 28, figs. 121–26; Baulez 1985, pp. 150–51; Kisluk-Grosheide 2006, pp. 27, 31, figs. 38, 39.

48. Armchair (*fauteuil à la reine*)

Paris, 1788
Georges Jacob (1739–1814); gilded by Louis-
François Chatard (ca. 1749–1819)
Carved and gilded walnut; gold brocaded silk
(not original)
H. 39⅜ in. (100 cm), w. 29½ in. (74.9 cm),
d. 25⅝ in. (65.1 cm)
Gift of J. Pierpont Morgan, 1907 (07.225.107)

A label pasted underneath the frame
identifies this armchair as having
been part of a large set of seat furniture (see detail below). Consisting of
more than sixty pieces, this set was
commissioned on October 31, 1787,
for Louis XVI's Salon des Jeux at
the Château de Saint-Cloud. The
menuisier Georges Jacob initially supplied eighteen armchairs, twelve with
straight backs meant to be placed
along the walls (*fauteuils meublants à
la reine*) and six with shaped backs for
use in the center of the room (*fauteuils
courants en cabriolet*). The number of
armchairs must have been thought
insufficient because on February 21,
1788, four more *fauteuils meublants à
la reine* were ordered for the gaming
room. Given the date on the label, the
Museum's example, stamped by
Jacob, is one of those later four.

Invoices for this set not only reflect
the division of labor among the different craftsmen but also reveal the
amount that each was paid. Jacob, who
cut the walnut to shape and joined the
various elements, charged 24 livres
for each armchair. A carver not mentioned by name was paid 180 livres
for the continuous-chain ornament
enclosing rosettes that embellishes the
frame. Most expensive of all was the
gilding done by Louis-François
Chatard, which amounted to 240

Label on the inside of the back seat rail

49

49, 50, 51. Daybed (*lit de repos* or *sultane*), armchair (*bergère*), and fire screen (*écran*)

livres and brought the total cost for the frame of each chair to 444 livres. Additional expenses were incurred for the upholstery by Claude-François Capin, who used a brocaded silk with a rosebush design against a green ground, now lost. With its simplicity of line and ornament from a classical vocabulary, this armchair is a textbook example of the Neoclassical style.

References: Lefuel 1923, pp. 161–69; Verlet 1994, pp. 239–43, 264–65, no. 38, ill.; Kisluk-Grosheide 2006, p. 37, fig. 58.

Paris, 1788
Made by Jean-Baptiste-Claude Séné (1748–1803); painted and gilded by Louis-François Chatard (ca. 1749–1819)
Carved, painted, and gilded walnut; modern cotton twill with silk embroidery
Daybed h. 36½ in. (92.7 cm), w. 69 in. (175.3 cm), d. 31½ in. (80 cm); armchair h. 39 in. (99.1 cm), w. 27¼ in. (69.2 cm), d. 25¼ in. (64.1 cm); fire screen h. 44¼ in. (112.4 cm), w. 27¾ in. (70.5 cm), d. (base) 17 in. (43.2 cm)
Gift of Ann Payne Blumenthal, 1941 (41.205.1–3a,b)

The Palace of St. Cloud belongs to the Duke of Orleans, is situated on the declivity of a mountain washed by the Seine. . . . The view from the house is delightful.

—Harry Peckham, *A Tour through Holland . . . and Part of France*

Louis XVI purchased the country residence of the duc d'Orléans a few miles west of Paris for Marie-Antoinette in 1785. Being in need of renovation, the palace was enlarged and altered for the queen, and many pieces of furniture were commissioned from Jean-Baptiste-Claude Séné. A member of an important dynasty of Parisian chairmakers, Séné had been appointed *menuisier* to the Crown in 1784.

A detailed 1788 description of this set, which also included four matching armchairs and a stool, indicates that the pieces were intended for one of Marie-Antoinette's private rooms at Saint-Cloud, her Cabinet Particulier. The frame of the daybed, originally

longer but shortened at a later date, is embellished with carving of ivy on the seat rail and garlands of roses along the crest rail. Ionic capitals surmount the short legs, and most remarkable of all are the Egyptian female half-figures on tapering supports that decorate the front stiles. Even though in his bill Sené called them simply caryatids, these figures clearly express the queen's taste for ornament derived from ancient Egyptian art, well before Napoléon's North African campaign made it fashionable. Similar ornament is found on the *bergère* (a comfortable armchair upholstered between the arms and the seat), which, in addition, has a medallion on top with Marie-Antoinette's initials framed by myrtle branches and roses. The matching screen, however, displays classical female figures on its feet and top rail. Unfortunately, the identity of the sculptor is not known, but Louis-François Chatard is documented as having painted and gilded the wooden surfaces.

The 1789 inventory of Saint-Cloud records the entire suite in the queen's Cabinet de Toilette, or dressing room. Listed by its show covers, as was customary for seat furniture, the set is described as being upholstered in white cotton twill, embroidered with a small floral ornament in silk. Known to have worked on needlepoint projects all her life, Marie-Antoinette did the embroidery herself, which she executed in satin stitch. Modern replicas of the queen's handiwork, including her interlaced monogram on the panel of the fire screen, grace the frames of the furniture today. The colorful floral embroidery on the light cotton ground conveys a sense of

51

summer, the season Marie-Antoinette preferred to spend at Saint-Cloud.

Epigraph. Peckham 1788, p. 199.

References: Verlet 1994, pp. 244–51, 265, no. 39, ill.; Kisluk-Grosheide 2006, pp. 36–37, figs. 50–55; Daniëlle O. Kisluk-Grosheide in Kisluk-Grosheide, Koeppe, and Rieder 2006, pp. 207–10, nos. 86–88, ill.

52, 53. Drop-front secretary on stand (*secrétaire à abattant* or *secrétaire en cabinet*) and commode (*commode à vantaux*)

Paris, ca. 1790
Adam Weisweiler (1744–1820)
Oak veneered with ebony, amaranth, holly, ebonized holly, satinwood, and Japanese and French lacquer panels; gilt-bronze mounts; brocatelle marble tops (not original); steel springs; morocco leather (not original)
Secretary h. 52⅜ in. (133 cm), w. 34 in. (86.1 cm), d. 16½ in. (41.9 cm); commode h. 38⅜ in. (97.5 cm), w. 58⅝ in. (148.9 cm), d. 22¼ in. (56.5 cm)
Gift of Mr. and Mrs. Charles Wrightsman, 1977 (1977.1.13, 12)

On October 7, 1790, many European royals and aristocrats were gathered in Frankfurt to attend the coronation of Leopold II as Holy Roman Emperor. Ferdinand IV (1751–1825), king of Naples, was among those present for this solemn event. Married to the new emperor's sister, Maria Carolina, Ferdinand was the brother-in-law of both Leopold and Marie-Antoinette. At this time of social and political instability caused by the French Revolution, the Parisian *marchand-mercier* Dominique Daguerre and his business partner, Martin-Eloi Lignereux, traveled to Frankfurt as well. They were looking for new clients and lucrative commissions. This secretary (or its pair) and a matching commode were among the luxury goods they brought along with them and offered for sale. Mounted with Japanese lacquer and exquisite gilt bronze, both pieces were purchased by the king of Naples, who ordered an additional secretary and a matching rolltop desk in 1792.[1] The set of furniture was placed in Ferdinand's study at the royal palace of Caserta. Jakob Philipp Hackert (1737–1807),

52

who as court painter to Ferdinand IV created gouaches for display in the king's study, described the interior in a letter of December 4, 1792, to his friend Count Dönhoff in Berlin:

"Everything is bronze and lacquer, the furniture is from Paris, the room is beautiful and splendid and cost thirty thousand ducats with all the decoration, which is simple but precious."[2]

53

The lacquer furniture was the work of Adam Weisweiler, who stamped the back of the secretary. He worked almost exclusively for *marchands-merciers* and especially for Dominique Daguerre, who supplied Weisweiler's Neoclassical furniture to an international clientele. The drawers of the breakfront commode, known as a *commode à vantaux* during the eighteenth century, are enclosed behind a double-hinged and bolted folding door to the right, and a single door to the left (see page 119, below). The sculptural half-figure corner mounts and those of the frieze, which include scrolling acanthus and ivy leaves, goats, and playful infant fauns, add a nearly unrivaled richness to this set of furniture. Because of their outstanding quality they have in the past been attributed to the bronze worker Pierre Gouthière (1732–1813). They might, however, equally well have been the work of François Rémond, who is known to have cast, finished, and gilded similar bronzes for Daguerre.

1. The second secretary is among the Museum's holdings (1971.1.14) and the rolltop desk is in a private collection.
2. The letter is cited, in part, in Nordhoff and Reimer 1994, vol. 2, p. 106, under no. 227.

References: Watson 1966b, pp. 191–94, no. 106a, ill., and pp. 133–38, no. 88, ill.; González-Palacios 2003, figs. 37–39, 41, 43; Daniëlle O. Kisluk-Grosheide in Kisluk-Grosheide, Koeppe, and Rieder 2006, pp. 210–13, no. 89, ill.

54. Side table (*commode servante* or *commode desserte*)

Paris, ca. 1790
Jean-Henri Riesener (1734–1806)
Oak, pine, mahogany, and mahogany veneer; gilt-bronze mounts; Carrara marble top and shelf
H. 36 in. (91.4 cm), w. 44⅜ in. (113.3 cm), d. 16¼ in. (41.3 cm)
Gift of Mr. and Mrs. Charles Wrightsman, 1977 (1977.102.8)

Known in French as a *commode servante* or *commode desserte*, this type of side table appears to have been born out of an increasing desire for privacy during the eighteenth century. Clean plates and the dessert course would be placed on the marble shelves, allowing the owner and his guests to dine without the presence of servants.

Stamped by Jean-Henri Riesener, this sideboard is one of several closely related pieces. The mahogany serves as a beautiful background for the gilt-bronze mounts in the form of almost lacelike ivy tendrils spiraling up the slender legs and scrolling foliage on the drawer fronts. Printed labels pasted underneath the table indicate that it was formerly at the Anichkov Palace in Saint Petersburg, where it is thought to have belonged to Empress Maria Feodorovna (1847–1928). As wife and later dowager empress of Alexander III (1845–1894), she lived in the palace from about 1866, the year of her marriage, until the Revolution of 1917. The table was among the French artworks acquired by the dealer Joseph Duveen during his visit to Soviet Russia. A nearly identical table, also with a Russian provenance, is in the collection of the Huntington Library, Art Collections, and Botanical Gardens, San Marino.

Reference: Watson 1966b, pp. 236–39, no. 122, ill.

Gilt Bronze and Mounted Porcelain

DANIËLLE KISLUK-GROSHEIDE AND JEFFREY MUNGER

I will not go further into the making of bronzes, because that is the task of workers other than the ébéniste. . . . *However, since it is the* ébénistes *who make the models to be cast, I cannot exhort them strongly enough to execute these with the greatest possible attention and care.*

—André-Jacob Roubo, *L'Art du menuisier*

Functional and exceedingly decorative *bronzes d'ameublement*, the so-called furnishing bronzes—wall lights, candelabra, and other types of lighting, firedogs (andirons), hearth fittings, and clocks—as well as gilt bronze mounts for porcelain and furniture, were an important aspect of the eighteenth-century decor. Well-known artists and sculptors designed them, closely following the latest styles. An elaborate guild system regulated the process of their creation and maintained high standards of craftsmanship. Consisting of many different steps, the manufacture of gilt-bronze objects was principally in the hands of the bronze workers, who were divided in eighteenth-century France into two guilds: that of the *fondeurs-ciseleurs*, or casters and chasers, and that of the *ciseleurs-doreurs*, or chasers and gilders. When the guild system was reformed in 1776, the casters and the gilders became members of a single guild.

Working from a drawing for a bronze object of simple design, a carver or sculptor would make a three-dimensional model in wood, clay, or wax. In preparation for casting, he would fashion a wax mold of the model. Then, having pressed the mold into a box filled with sand, he would pour molten bronze, an alloy of copper and tin, into the resulting depression. For a more complex design, the cire perdue, or lost-wax, process was used. In this technique, the wax model was fashioned around a core made of plaster or clay and then covered with plaster or clay to form a mold. The mold was then dried and fired to melt the wax, which flowed out through tiny holes in the mold. The empty space left by the wax was filled with molten bronze. The metal cooled and hardened, and any imperfections in the rough cast were cleaned up in a process called *reparure*. The actual finishing was done by the *ciseleur*, who tooled the bronzes with his instruments, creating burnished areas and a variety of finely or coarsely pounced or grained surfaces. This stage in the manufacture of bronzes was extremely important because chasing would lend the objects vitality through the varying ways that the sun or flickering candlelight would be reflected off the differently finished surfaces. The various bronze workers rarely signed their work, but their names are sometimes revealed in bills or other contemporary documents.

A final step in the manufacture of furnishing bronzes was mercury gilding, and it added a substantial cost to the price of an object. The bronze surface was coated with a mixture of mercury and ground gold, or *or moulu* (hence "ormolu," the English name for gilt bronze) and heated over an open fire. The gold adhered to the base metal, and the mercury evaporated, creating dangerous fumes. The process was repeated several times until a gold layer of sufficient thickness had been achieved. The piece could be left matte or was burnished with a heliotrope stone. Many objects, however, were not mercury-gilded, but simply cleaned by immersion in acid and then lacquered with a clear or yellow varnish to give them the appearance of gold.

During the eighteenth century, the most sophisticated *bronzes d'ameublement* and those of the highest quality were made and sold in Paris, largely in the fashionable shops of the *marchands-merciers*, located on the rue Saint-Honoré and nearby streets. Even though these luxury dealers did not make any furniture or furnishings them-

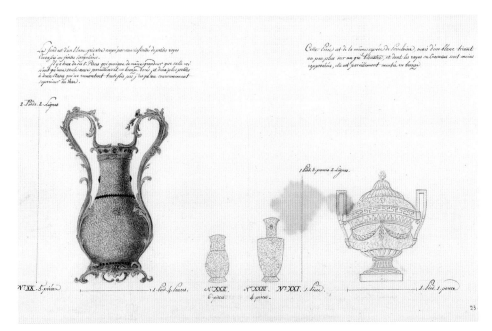

Fig. 44. *Design for Four Vases*,
ca. 1770-85. Pen and brown
ink, watercolor, and black
chalk. The Metropolitan
Museum of Art, New York,
Gift of Raphael Esmerian, 1961
(61.680.1.10).

selves, they played a role in their design. Furthermore, the *marchands-merciers* arranged for any upkeep or repair and, in the case of bronzes, for any regilding or relacquering. In January 1754, for instance, the dealer Lazare Duvaux charged 42 livres for redipping four pairs of wall lights for Madame de Pompadour in order to "make them like new."[1]

It was the practice of these dealers and trendsetters—and a very lucrative one—to embellish Asian as well as European porcelains with gilt-bronze handles, bases, and rims (see fig. 44). In this way the exotic pieces were adapted to the European aesthetic and a damaged or mediocre piece of porcelain could be ingeniously enhanced. The choicest luxury goods offered by the *marchands-merciers* were the figures, bowls, and other porcelain objects that had been transformed into cande-

labra, inkstands, or potpourri vessels by the addition of gilt-bronze mounts and Vincennes porcelain flowers. Visiting the shopkeepers to examine their stock of such novelties was an enjoyable and much-practiced pastime. For instance, in May 1782, Henriette Louise de Waldner de Freundstein, the baronne d'Oberkirch (1754–1803), went to the Petit Dunkerque, the Paris establishment of Charles-Raymond Granchez near the Pont Neuf, where she spent several agreeable hours. She reported in her diary that the place was filled with trinkets of every kind and that there were often so many shoppers that a guard had to be posted near the entrance.[2]

DK-G

Epigraph. Roubo 1769–75, vol. 3, pt. 4 (1774), p. 1028.

1. Duvaux 1748–58/1965, vol. 2, p. 190.
2. Oberkirch 1789/1970, p. 172.

55. Pair of candlesticks (*flambeaux* or *chandeliers*)

Paris, 1735–50
After designs by Juste-Aurèle Meissonnier
(1695–1750)
Gilt bronze
H. 12⅛ in. (30.8 cm)
Gift of Mrs. Charles Wrightsman, 1999
(1999.370.1a,b, 2a,b)

In the era before gas lighting and electricity, candles played a principal role in illuminating the interior of a house. The number of candles lit was an indication of the status of the owner; beeswax candles, preferred over tallow because they burned cleaner and had a more pleasant smell, were enormously expensive. No wonder, then, that visitors commented on the quantity of light at certain events—as Philip Thicknesse did in his *Useful Hints to Those Who Make the Tour of France* (1768). The table at a dinner he attended in 1767 "was illuminated with upwards of sixty wax lights."[1]

The exuberantly asymmetrical model for this candlestick was the work of Juste-Aurèle Meissonnier, one of the leading Rococo designers. Active also as architect, painter, and silversmith to Louis XV, Meissonnier rendered three drawings in order to show from all sides this candlestick with its loosely spiraling stem. The drawings were engraved by Gabriel Huquier (1695–1772) and published in *Dousième Livre des oeuvres de J. A. Messonnier: Livre de chandeliers de sculpture en argent* (1734–35).[2] The design, incorporating shells, floral sprays, and even a butterfly in a whirlwind of motion, became very popular and was executed in both silver and gilt bronze. The quality of the chasing and gilding of this pair with its burnished and matte areas is outstanding.   DK-G

1. Thicknesse 1768, p. 41.
2. Fuhring 1999, vol. 2, pp. 350–52, nos. 76–78, ill.

References: Watson 1966c, p. 332, no. 163a–d, ill.; William Rieder in "Recent Acquisitions" 2000, p. 32, ill.

56. Wall clock
(*pendule en cartel*)

Paris, ca. 1740–45
Case by Charles Cressent (1685–1768); movement by Jean Godde the Elder (ca. 1668–1748/49)
Case: oak with marquetry of brass and tortoiseshell; gilt bronze; enamel dial with enameled
numerals; brass and steel movement
H. 52½ in. (133.4 cm), w. 24½ in. (62.2 cm),
d. 15½ in. (39.4 cm)
Gift of Mr. and Mrs. Charles Wrightsman, 1971
(1971.206.27)

The theme of this magnificent
Rococo wall clock with its asymmetrical design is the triumph of love
over time. As the son of a sculptor
and grandson of an *ébéniste*, Charles
Cressent, who made the case, combined the talents of both and created
not only outstanding case furniture
but also highly imaginative sculpture
in the form of *bronzes d'ameublement*.
Firedogs, clock cases, wall lights, and
mounts for furniture were cast and
finished in his workshop, violating
the rules of the bronze casters' and
bronze gilders' guilds, to which
Cressent, as a furniture maker, did
not belong. As a result, three times
during his life, legal proceedings were
brought against him for employing
casters, chasers, and gilders in his
workshops. Financial difficulties
forced him to organize three sales of
his possessions, the first of which was
held in 1749. The catalogues for these
sales included detailed descriptions of
the offered works, which allow the
identification of certain clock models.
Lot 25 of the 1749 catalogue, for
instance, seems identical in its design
to the Museum's clock, of which several other examples are extant. The
description mentions the winged

57

putto, symbolizing love, at the cresting, seated on clouds and resting his elbow on an hourglass, while Father Time with his scythe reclines on the chaos of the world below. Also noted are the two large trees that frame the case and the fact that everything was beautifully chased and gilded. There is no reference to the sides of the clock case. They are veneered with marquetry of tortoiseshell and brass, so-called Boulle work, showing that Cressent was a master cabinetmaker as well. The movement is signed "Jean Godde L'aisné A Paris." Godde was one of several makers of clocks or watches by that name, and little is known about him.   DK-G

References: Watson 1966c, pp. 357–59, no. 182, ill.; Dell 1967, pp. 213, 214, figs. 34, 37; Penelope Hunter in Metropolitan Museum of Art 1975, pp. 258–59, ill.; Pradère 2003, pp. 186, 299, no. 228, ill.

57. Pair of potpourri bowls with cover

France, ca. 1745–50
Bowls: Japanese porcelain, late 17th century
Mounts: French gilt bronze, ca. 1745–50
H. 15⅛ in. (38.4 cm), w. 16¼ in. (41.3 cm), d. 10¼ in. (26 cm)
Gift of Mr. and Mrs. Charles Wrightsman, 1979 (1979.396.2a,b, 3a,b)

Japanese porcelains with French mounts from the mid-eighteenth century are less common than mounted Chinese porcelains of the same period. Porcelains from Japan were sometimes chosen for mounting in silver in the first part of the century, but it seems that within several decades Chinese porcelains embellished with gilt bronze became the preferred choice of European collectors. Not only are surviving examples of mounted Chinese porcelains more numerous than their Japanese counterparts but the former appear with greater frequency in eighteenth-century auction catalogues and inventories.

These covered porcelain bowls were produced at Arita, in southwestern Japan, in the late seventeenth century. Their decoration displaying highly stylized vegetation and rock work is in the Kakiemon style, named after a family of potters working in Arita whose wares were commonly painted in a palette dominated by red, deep blue, turquoise, and yellow. The appearance of these bowls has been transformed by the addition of gilt-bronze mounts in the full-blown Rococo style. The design of the mounts incorporates sinuous C-shaped scrolls, elongated acanthus leaves, and bulrushes, and the asymmetrical upward curve of the cover mount imparts the sense of movement that characterizes the best Rococo design. The cartouche-shaped openings in the gilt-bronze rim that separates the cover from the bowl suggest that these pieces were used as containers for petals, herbs, and spices to scent the air, but it is likely that they were intended primarily to be decorative. They would have been viewed as important works of art, and both their imposing size and the high cost of the Japanese porcelain and the mounts would have signaled the owner's elevated financial status.   JM

References: Watson 1966c, pp. 442–43, no. 249a, b, ill.; Dauterman 1970, pp. 395–97, no. 176a, b, ill.

58. Set of four three-light sconces (*bras de lumière*)

Paris, ca. 1750
Gilt bronze
H. 28¾ in. (73 cm), w. 22⅞ in. (58.1 cm), d. 13¼ in. (33.6 cm)
Gift of Mr. and Mrs. Charles Wrightsman, 1972 (1972.284.10–13)

Gilt bronze was used extensively for different types of lighting, ranging from freestanding candlesticks and candelabra to hanging chandeliers and lanterns. Sconces were usually placed on either side of a mirror so that the flames of their candles were reflected and multiplied in the glass. Given their size, these examples, which were originally part of a set of six,[1] must have been intended for a large, formal room. Three scrolling arms spring organically from a shaped stem, which incorporates

floral trails, fruit-bearing olive branches, and rocaille ornament. The candleholders at the ends of the arms are in the form of spiraling foliage, and their drip pans resemble acanthus leaves. The sconces complement each other symmetrically and form two proper pairs. Each one consists of a number of separate elements, fastened in such a way that it appears as if they

were cast as a single piece. The virtuosity of their design and the symphony of flowing lines and twirling movement make this set of beautifully chased and gilded wall lights a triumph of Rococo art.   DK-G

1. The other two are in the collection of the Toledo Museum of Art, Toledo, Ohio.

Reference: Watson 1966c, p. 416, no. 229a–d, ill.

58

59. Microscope

Paris, ca. 1750
Optical elements by Claude-Siméon Passemant
(1702–1769)
Gilt bronze, shagreen, tinted parchment with
gold tooling, steel, brass, mahogany, mirror
glass, glass
H. fully extended 24¼ in. (61.6 cm), w. and
d. 10¾ in. (27.3 cm)
Purchase, Mr. and Mrs. Charles Wrightsman
Gift and Gift of Mr. and Mrs. Charles
Wrightsman, by exchange, 1986 (1986.1a–d)

Qualifying both as a work of art and
as a scientific instrument, this microscope exemplifies beautifully the
broad interests of mid-eighteenth-
century amateurs who dabbled in the
sciences to explore the mysteries of
the natural world. This compound
microscope contains three convex
lenses in its inner cylinder, which fits
into a wooden tube covered with
green shagreen, an animal or fish
skin, in this case from the tropical
stingray *Dasyatis* (or *Trygon*) *sephen*.
The three white "pearls" visible on
the shaft of the microscope originally
marked the center of the ray's back
and hide (see fig. 45). Polished and
often tinted green, the attractive
granular surface of ray- and sharkskin
was fashionable in mid-eighteenth-
century France for the decoration of
small cases, snuffboxes, and other
luxurious objects.

   In order to use the instrument, the
ornamental gilt-bronze finial must be
unscrewed, thus giving access to the
eyepiece and allowing the owner to
look at a specimen under magnifica-
tion. Claude-Siméon Passemant, who
was scientific instrument maker to
Louis XV and worked in lodgings in
the Palais du Louvre, provided the
optical elements. Known for the

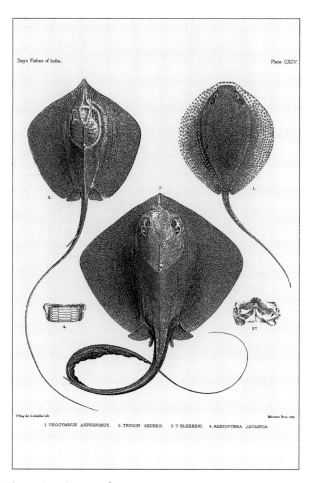

creation of clocks, celestial and terrestrial globes, telescopes, and barometers, Passemant signed the base "Passemant au Louvre." The metalworker responsible for the graceful tripod stand with its C-scroll and inverted C-scroll decoration in gilt bronze has not been identified. Still functional, this piece may have belonged to the king himself, who was interested in physics, chemistry, and botany. A series of prints depicting scientific instruments in the royal collection kept at the Château de la Muette shows three different views of a microscope that is very similar, if not identical, to this one (see fig. 46).

DK-G

Reference: James Parker in Metropolitan Museum of Art 1986, pp. 26–27, ill.

Fig. 45. Francis Day and C. Achilles, *Urogymnus Asperrimus, Trygon Sephen, T. Bleekeri, Rhinoptera Javanica,* plate CXCV in Francis Day, *The Fishes of India,* vol. 2 (London, 1878).

Fig. 46. Guillaume Dheulland, plate XIX in *Suitte de XXI. Planches Gravees sous la Direction de Dom Noel. Garde du Cabinet Royal de Physique. Representant les Elevations et Couppes de plusieurs Telescopes et Microscopes, quis se voyant audit Cabinet a Passy,* ca. 1772. Engraving. Bibliothèque Nationale de France, Paris, Département des Estampes et de la Photographie.

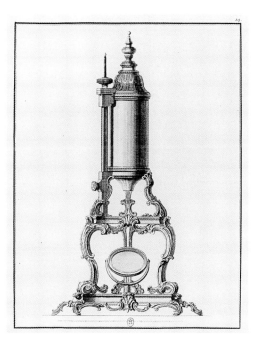

60. Pair of three-light candelabra (*candélabres* or *girandoles*)

Paris, ca. 1750
Birds: Meissen, Germany, after models attributed to Johann Joachim Kändler (1706–1775)
Hard-paste porcelain
Mounts: Paris
Gilt bronze
(.3) h. 23 in. (58.4 cm); (.4) h. 22 in. (55.9 cm)
Bequest of Mrs. Robert Lehman, 2006
(2007.90.3, 4)

Trained as a sculptor, Johann Joachim Kändler joined the porcelain manufactory in Meissen, near Dresden, as a modeler in 1731. A prolific and talented artist, Kändler supplied the workshops there with numerous models, ranging from small figural

60

groups to table services and decorative wares. Among his most celebrated achievements were the animal figures he created for the Japanese Palace in Dresden at the behest of Augustus the Strong, elector of Saxony (1670–1733), which included many native European and exotic birds. These figures were based either on live specimens observed at the royal menagerie at Moritzburg or on stuffed ones preserved in the local natural-history collection, and they illustrate the contemporary fascination with the natural world. In March 1735, for the Japanese Palace, Kändler modeled his first bittern, an elusive long-necked

bird that moves through the reeds along the shore stalking fish. Different, smaller models of bittern by the artist seem to have been popular during the mid-eighteenth century, and multiple pairs are known today. With their attractive gray and brown plumage and dark streaks, the graceful heronlike birds strut on mounds embellished with a thicket of water plants and rushes.

In Paris various Meissen porcelain birds were combined with fanciful gilt-bronze mounts to make exquisite candelabra such as these, for which the *marchands-merciers* asked steep prices. Lazare Duvaux's account book lists

several pairs of three-light *girandoles* that were sold between 1748 and 1751. Two of them incorporated Meissen swans, and the third, unidentified Meissen porcelain birds.[1] A pair of bittern with identical scrolling mounts are in the Huntington Library, Art Collections, and Botanical Gardens in San Marino. They may originally have formed a set of four candelabra with the Museum's pair.   DK-G

1. Duvaux 1748–58/1965, vol. 2, pp. 7, 71, 77.

Reference: Linda Strauss and Martin Chapman in Bennett and Sargentson 2008, pp. 166–67, no. 62, ill. (the pair in the Huntington Library).

61. Mounted vase

France, ca. 1750
Vase: Chinese porcelain, early 18th century
Mounts: French gilt bronze, ca. 1750
H. 23 ⅜ in. (59.4 cm), w. 13 ¾ in. (34.9 cm),
d. 12 ½ in. (31.8 cm)
Gift of Mr. and Mrs. Charles Wrightsman, 1971
(1971.206.22)

*With delight one notices . . . a very
large number of pieces of old porcelain
of the greatest perfection, [and] the
mounts that accompany the pieces seem
to rival them in value.*

—Antoine-Nicolas Dézallier d'Argenville,
Voyage pittoresque de Paris

In eighteenth-century France, gilt
bronze played important functional
and decorative roles in the houses of
those who could afford it. Gilt bronze
was employed for andirons, furniture
hardware, wall lights, candelabra, and
chandeliers, and it served as an embellishment for porcelain produced both
in Asia and in Europe. This large
Chinese porcelain vase with unusually
elaborate and sculptural gilt-bronze
mounts offers a spectacular example of
the transformation that can be effected
by the addition of mounts. The profile
of the vase is radically changed, and
the profusion of curving metal shapes
creates a quintessential expression of
French Rococo taste.

The cost of gilt-bronze mounts
was considerable, and an object of this
scale would have been very expensive.
Eighteenth-century auction catalogues indicate that mounted vases
such as this were frequently found in
aristocratic collections, and the prices
they realized upon their sale demonstrate that they retained their value
even after the style of their mounts

had passed from the forefront of fashion. In the 1782 sale of the art collection of Louis-Marie-Augustin, duc
d'Aumont, many of the lots offered
were either Japanese or Chinese

mounted porcelains, and a number of
them were bought by Louis XVI for
substantial sums.   JM

Epigraph. Dézallier d'Argenville 1757, p. 281.

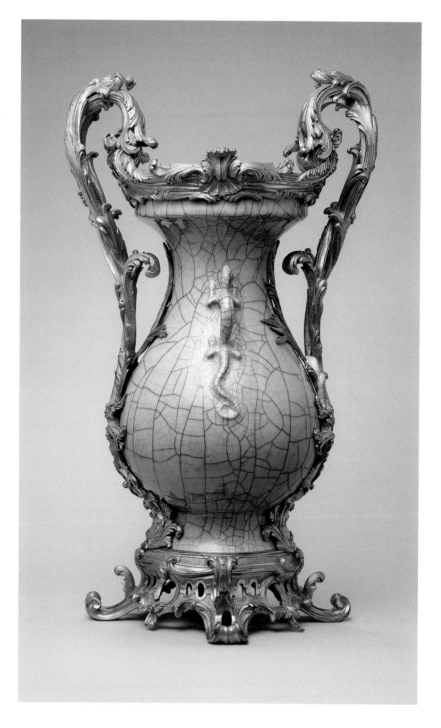

62. Pair of mounted vases

France, ca. 1760–70
Vases: Chinese porcelain, early 18th century
Mounts: French gilt bronze, ca. 1760–70
H. 12¼ in. (32.4 cm), w. 6½ in. (16.5 cm),
d. 4⅞ in. (12.4 cm)
The Jules Bache Collection, 1949 (49.7.80, 81)

Chinese porcelain vases decorated
with a celadon glaze enjoyed great
popularity among French art collectors
of the eighteenth century (see fig. 47).
Frequently they were fitted in France
with gilt-bronze mounts that served to
enhance the porcelain in the eyes of
the potential buyer. The *marchands-
merciers*, who did so much to influence
eighteenth-century French taste, were
usually responsible for commissioning

Fig. 47. Henri-Pierre
Danloux, *The Baron de
Besenval in His Salon
de Compagnie*, 1791. Oil
on canvas, 18⅜ × 14⅝ in.
(46.5 × 37 cm). The
National Gallery, London,
Bought, 2004 (NG6598).

the gilt-bronze mounts, which were required to closely fit the shape of the vase. In the case of this pair of vases, the design of the mounts includes both Rococo and Neoclassical motifs, suggesting a date of manufacture between 1760 and 1770, a period of transition between the two styles. The mounts incorporate putti, floral swags, shells, and scrolling vegetation, all unrelated stylistically to the vase's molded designs, which echo the decoration of archaic Chinese bronzes. Typically they venerate the Chinese porcelains while substantially transforming their appearance, creating a luxury object that is entirely French in taste. It is likely that this pair of vases was once owned by the great English collector William Beckford (1760–1844), who may have acquired them because of their strong association with eighteenth-century French aristocratic taste. JM

Reference: Jeffrey Munger in Ostergard 2001, pp. 328–29, no. 46, ill.

63. Pair of three-light sconces (*bras de lumière*)

Paris, ca. 1775
Gilt bronze
H. 11½ in. (29.2 cm), w. 19½ in. (49.5 cm),
d. 12½ in. (31.8 cm)
Gift of Mr. and Mrs. Charles Wrightsman, 1973
(1973.315.10, 11)

These wall lights are shaped with great naturalism to resemble lily stalks tied together with a large bow (see detail page 134). They are not a proper pair, as their ribbons do not complement each other but flow in the same direction; therefore, they were

63

63 (detail)

64. Vase on a column stand

Versailles, after 1771–72
Design probably by François-Joseph Bélanger
(1744–1818); lapidary work probably by
Augustin Bocciardi (ca. 1729–1797)
Egyptian porphyry
Mounts: Paris, ca. 1780
Attributed to Pierre-Philippe Thomire
(1751–1843)
Gilt bronze
H. of vase 41¼ in. (104.8 cm); h. of stand 35⅝ in.
(90.5 cm); diam. 16⅜ in. (41.6 cm)
Gift of Mr. and Mrs. Charles Wrightsman, 1971
(1971.206.44)

most likely part of a larger set. The unknown chaser and gilder made clear contrasts between such highly burnished areas as the opened blooms and those given a matte finish, such as the buds. Lilies are strongly scented flowers that were very popular during the Neoclassical period, and a number of contemporary references to sconces in the shape of sprays of lilies are known. The successful bronze worker Pierre Gouthière, for instance, made a pair composed of three lily branches for Madame du Barry, mistress of Louis XV, for which he charged 2,500 livres. Horace Walpole reported in a letter of September 9, 1775, to Anne Liddell, that the Grand Cabinet of Madame de Mirepoix's Parisian hôtel was "illuminated by four branches of lilies of ormolu, each as loose and graceful as that which Guido [Reni]'s angel holds in the 'Salutation' [*Annunciation*] at [the church of] the Carmelites."[1]

DK-G

1. Walpole 1937–83, vol. 32 (1965), p. 261.

References: *France in the Eighteenth Century* 1968, p. 148, no. 886a, b; Francis J. B. Watson in Watson and Dauterman 1970, pp. 76–77, no. 308a, b, ill.

Louis-Marie-Augustin, duc d'Aumont, assembled an impressive collection of marble and hardstone vases, urns, columns, and other artworks. After a visit on October 10, 1775, to the duke's Paris residence, Horace Walpole noted admiringly in his journal: "2 millions in tables, columns, lustres and china. 2 beautiful porphyry tables with legs of same in ormolu exquisite by Gouthière who works only for him."[1] Most of those luxurious furnishings were sold at a public auction following the owner's death. According to the sale catalogue, the duke had assiduously hunted down the rarest marbles and hardstones in Rome and throughout Italy. Those materials had been transported to Versailles, where Aumont had established a stone-cutting workshop at the Hôtel des Menus-Plaisirs, the office responsible for organizing the court entertainments. François-Joseph Bélanger, a prominent architect and designer, was the artistic director of the workshop, and it is very likely that he was responsible for the design of this imposing vase and its base, which are almost certainly

carved from a single column found at an ancient Roman ruin. Unlike the mounts of the porphyry tables seen by Walpole, the gilt-bronze decoration of the Museum's vase and column is not attributed to Gouthière but to the sculptor and bronze worker Pierre-Philippe Thomire. The ram's-head handles and swags of vine leaves and grapes that embellish the vase are symbolic of the wine god Bacchus.

DK-G

1. Walpole 1937–83, vol. 7 (1939), p. 353.

References: *France in the Eighteenth Century* 1968, p. 148, no. 887; Watson 1969, p. 188, pl. IV; Francis J. B. Watson in Watson and Dauterman 1970, pp. 70–74, no. 306, ill.; Wolfram Koeppe in Koeppe 2008, pp. 280–81, no. 102, ill.

65. Mantel clock (*pendule de cheminée*)

Paris, ca. 1783
Design by François-Joseph Bélanger
(1744–1818); model possibly by Louis-Simon
Boizot (1743–1809); case attributed to Pierre
Gouthière (1732–1813); movement by the work-
shop of Jean-Baptiste Lepaute (1727–1802) and
Pierre-Henry, called Henry, Lepaute (1749–1806)
Gilt bronze, marble, and painted metal; enamel
dial; brass and steel movement
H. 21 in. (53.3 cm), w. 21½ in. (54.6 cm),
d. 6½ in. (16.5 cm)
Gift of Mr. and Mrs. Charles Wrightsman, 1972
(1972.284.16)

Capturing daily life in the French
capital on the eve of the Revolution, the
playwright Louis-Sébastien Mercier
(1780–1814) observed in *Tableau de
Paris*: "Every chimney-piece has its
clock; a pity, I think; a dismal fashion.
Nothing is more dreary to contem-
plate than a clock; you watch your life
ebbing, the pendulum ticks off each

second that is yours only as it passes,
and then is yours no more. Clocks
are everywhere, in every room you
see them, and apparently nobody
finds them disturbing, though they
mark most mercilessly the flight of
the hours; clocks like little temples,
or with domes of gilded bronze, or
perhaps globes of white marble, with
figures running round like an equa-
tor. . . . Luxury has run the whole
gamut of imagination in devising
these superfluous splendours, it can
go no further; and since they are quite
useless, and not even pleasing to the
eye, the waste of money in such futile
expenditure is heartbreaking."[1]

Would Mercier have been equally
critical of the Museum's timepiece, its
movement resting on a tasseled cushion placed on the backs of two winged
sphinxes? The cresting of the case
alludes to love: a pair of billing doves
perches on clouds from which spill

flowers, mostly roses and myrtle
branches, both sacred to Venus. The
sphinxes recline on a white marble
base with semicircular ends that are
embellished with garlands of fruit and
flowers. The recessed tolework panel
in front encloses medallions depicting
six of the twelve zodiac signs. With
their striated wigs, the sphinxes are
expressions of the budding interest in
a novel form of decoration inspired by
art from ancient Egypt. A clock of
nearly this exact model was supplied
for use in the salon at Bagatelle, the
pleasure pavilion built in just sixty-
three days for the comte d'Artois,
whose sister-in-law Marie-Antoinette
had wagered that the work could not
be finished in less than three months.
The architect Bélanger provided
designs not only for the building but
also for many of its interior furnishings, which took longer to complete,
however. A contemporary document
pertaining to the Bagatelle clock provides a date of 1783, gives the name of
the designer Bélanger, and identifies
Pierre Gouthière, an exceptionally
fine bronze worker, as the chaser and
gilder. Gouthière was known for a
special type of gilding with a matte
finish that creates a lively effect when
set next to burnished areas, as seen on
the Museum's clock. The movement is
by the Lepaute workshop, a distinguished firm of clockmakers consisting of various family members by that
name, which appears on the dial.

DK-G

1. Mercier 1781–88/1999, pp. 228–29.

References: Edey 1982, pp. 82, 85, no. 77, ill.
p. 84; Ottomeyer and Pröschel 1986, vol. 1,
p. 281, no. 4.13.4, ill. p. 280; Verlet 1987,
p. 304, fig. 338; Hughes 1996, vol. 1, p. 507,
under no. 112.

66. Musical mantel clock (*pendule de cheminée*)

Paris, ca. 1784
Jean-Baptiste-André Furet (ca. 1720–1807)
Gilt and enameled bronze; marble; enamel; brass and steel movement
H. 29 in. (73.7 cm), w. 16¼ in. (41.3 cm), d. 9 in. (22.9 cm)
Gift of Samuel H. Kress Foundation, 1958
(58.75.127)

One of the most remarkable clocks in the Museum is this one shaped like the bust of an African princess. The unusual model had already attracted attention during the late eighteenth century, according to a description in the anonymous chronicle *Mémoires secrets*, for July 4, 1784: "The curious are going to M. Furet's shop in the rue Saint-Honoré to see three extra-ordinary clocks of his creation. The first represents the bust of a negress exceptionally made. . . . Upon pulling one ear-ring the hour is described in the right eye and the minutes in the left. Upon pulling the other a musical movement plays a succession of airs."[1] This particular clock was not long afterward acquired for the royal col-lection, but the model was repeated several times with small variations. One of them, signed by Furet, clock-maker to the king, is the Museum's version. The dark, enameled surface of the bust contrasts beautifully with the clothing and accoutrements of gilt bronze, such as the turban with its tuft of plumes and the fur-trimmed robe, as well as the openwork ear-rings, the string of graduated beads, the floral garland, and the bow and quiver. Whereas the head and chest contain the clock movement, the marble plinth below serves as a case for the

66 (detail)

67. Twelve-light chandelier (*lustre*)

Paris, ca. 1785
Attributed to François Rémond (1747–1812)
Varnished copper alloy, gilt bronze
H. 55 in. (139.7 cm), diam. 28½ in. (72.4 cm)
Gift of Mr. and Mrs. Charles Wrightsman, 1972
(1972.242)

The metal body of this graceful chandelier is composed of a vase fitted with a slender, spiral-fluted neck of gilt bronze, topped by an arrangement of various fruits. Two pairs of S-shaped candle branches emerge from the folded arms of two beautifully modeled female half-figures evolving from acanthus leaves (see detail far right), while additional branches spring from between the horns of two satyr masks. The combination of varnished metal and gilt bronze offers the kind of rich and sophisticated contrast favored during the late eighteenth century. This chandelier has been attributed to the bronze worker François Rémond, based on similarities with some of his documented work. A highly successful artist, Rémond worked for the *marchand-mercier* Dominique Daguerre and was patronized by the comte d'Artois and Marie-Antoinette. Several variants of this model are known; a closely related chandelier is in the collection of the Musée Nissim de Camondo, Paris.   DK-G

Reference: Parker and Le Corbeiller 1979, p. 102, ill. p. 106.

musical movement, a tiny pipe organ, which could once be activated by pulling the earring on the figure's right ear but no longer functions. That such musical movements were delicate is illustrated by the fact that the example at the French court was already in need of repair three times during the late eighteenth century.

The passage of time is not usually visible in this highly decorative clock. On the hour, the music would play and the eyes would open, showing the hour in roman numerals (I–XII) in the woman's right eye and the minutes in arabic numerals (2–60) in the left. However, by pulling the earring on her left ear the eyes could be opened at any time.   DK-G

1. *Mémoires secrets* 1786, p. 78.

References: Parker 1960a, pp. 306–7, fig. 38; James Parker in Dauterman, Parker, and Standen 1964, pp. 268–72, no. 65, figs. 226–28.

68. Pair of ivory vases (*vases en ivoire*)

Paris, ca. 1786
Ivory; gilt-bronze mounts
H. 15 in. (38.1 cm), w. 9 in. (22.9 cm), d. 6½ in.
(16.5 cm)
Bequest of George Blumenthal, 1941
(41.190.59a,b, 60a,b)

Ivory-turning had been a fashionable pastime at European courts during the sixteenth and early seventeenth centuries, and it was revived in France and elsewhere during the second half of the eighteenth century. Louis XV worked the lathe himself, and his daughters received instruction in this art form. His grandson the dauphin, the future Louis XVI, also took lessons, as did his brothers. A group of ivory vases was recorded at the Château de Versailles on the eve of the Revolution, possibly created by members of the royal family. It is more likely, however, that Michel Voisin (1729–1786), turning master to Louis XVI, or his son François was responsible for these precious, lace-like objects. A series of engraved designs by the younger Voisin, entitled *Nouveau Cahier de vases*, *composés par Voisin Fils*, includes a vase that is similar to but more elaborate than the Museum's pair. The chief difference is that the body and shoulder of the Museum's covered vases are decorated with vertical openwork channels instead of spiraling ones. As suggested in the engraving, the Museum's vessels are richly embellished with gilt-bronze mounts. Especially noteworthy are the beautifully modeled female busts and the scrolling handles shaped like interlaced branches of berried ivy (see frontispiece, page ii).

Since the eighteenth-century provenance of the Museum's pair remains a mystery, one can only wonder if they were part of the ivory collection at Versailles. Nine such vases were also documented in the Cabinet Intérieur of the king's aunt Madame Victoire at the Château de Bellevue in

1786, displayed in individual glass cases. The presence of such protective cases suggests that these exotic open-work vessels were purely decorative and considered too delicate for use as potpourri holders. DK-G

References: Parker and Le Corbeiller 1979, p. 108, ill. p. 109; Bertrand Rondot in *Marie-Antoinette* 2008, p. 185, under no. 127.

69. Set of four three-light sconces (*bras de lumière*)

Paris, ca. 1787–88
Gilt bronze
H. 32 in. (81.3 cm), w. 15 in. (38.1 cm), d. 10¼ in. (26 cm)
Gift of Mr. and Mrs. Charles Wrightsman, 1973 (1973.315.6–9)

Music was one of Marie-Antoinette's lifelong diversions. She was taught to perform and sing when young in Vienna, where the opera composer Christoph Willibald Gluck (1714–1787) was her tutor. She amused herself with music several hours a day at the French court and was a devotee of the opera. The queen's enjoyment of music is reflected in the design of these wall lights, which were ordered probably in 1787 or the following year for her use at the Château de Saint-Cloud. Although no precise date or authorship have been established for them, they can easily be recognized among the furnishings listed as in the queen's Cabinet Intérieur in the detailed inventory description of the summer castle drawn up in 1789.

Suspended from a gilt-bronze ribbon tied in a bowknot, the back plate of the sconces is shaped like a lyre with a pendant trophy of musical instruments. In addition to music, the decoration also alludes to Bacchus, the Roman deity of wine and drunken revelry who was also patron of viticulture, and who is frequently shown in the company of satyrs dancing to music. Two of the arms are shaped as cornucopias with scrolls and garlands of vine leaves and grapes, their candle dishes piled up with fruit. A satyr mask and thyrsus, the staff topped by a pinecone, an attribute of Bacchus, join the trophy of musical instruments.

DK-G

References: *France in the Eighteenth Century* 1968, p. 148, no. 884a, b; Francis J. B. Watson in Watson and Dauterman 1970, pp. 78–81, no. 309a–d, ill.; Ottomeyer and Pröschel 1986, vol. 1, p. 242, no. 4.5.10, ill.

70. Set of four three-light sconces (*bras de lumière*)

Paris, 1788
Cast by either Étienne-Jean Forestier (d. 1768) or his brother Pierre-Auguste Forestier; chased and gilded by Pierre-Philippe Thomire (1751–1843), under the direction of Jean Hauré (b. 1739)
Gilt bronze
H. 21¾ in. (55.2 cm), w. 18 in. (45.7 cm), d. 10⅞ in. (27.6 cm)
Gift of Mr. and Mrs. Charles Wrightsman, 1979 (1979.172.3–6)

This set of wall lights was adapted from an existing model in order to match the decor of Louis XVI's bed-chamber at the Château de Saint-

Cloud, for which the four wall lights were commissioned. First executed for Marc-Antoine Thierry, baron de Ville d'Avray (1732–1792), who had been in charge of the royal furnishings as head of the Garde-Meuble de la Couronne since 1783, the original design incorporated a ram's head holding a garland of vine leaves and bunches of grapes in its mouth, below a flower vase. For Louis XVI's set, the ram's head was replaced by that of a lion, the king of animals and a symbol of power. A lion also served as a decorative motif on the bed and seat furniture in the same room. Since the rest of the design was not altered, the lions appear, curiously enough, to be

70 (detail)

eating grapes, as if they had turned herbivorous for the occasion (see detail page 142).

According to extant bills, the bronze caster Forestier, either Étienne-Jean or his brother Pierre-Auguste, was paid 204 livres for his work. Pierre-Philippe Thomire charged 820 livres for chasing and 1,200 livres for gilding these unique sconces, bringing the total cost to 2,224 livres for the set of four. Almost immediately after the wall lights were delivered, in April 1788, they were replaced by others and are therefore not listed in the king's bedroom in the inventory of Saint-Cloud that was drawn up the following year.

DK-G

References: Watson 1966c, p. 426, no. 237a–d, ill.; Verlet 1967, pp. 210–11; Verlet 1987, p. 330 and p. 47, fig. 42.

71 (detail)

71. Pair of seven-light candelabra (*candélabres* or *girandoles*)

France, ca. 1790
Gilt bronze, griotte marble, bardiglio marble
H. 47⅜ in. (120.5 cm), w. 19¾ in. (50.3 cm), d. 13¼ in. (34.9 cm)
Gift of Mr. and Mrs. Charles Wrightsman, 1973 (1973.315.4, 5)

Candelabra became more and more elaborate during the course of the eighteenth century and were frequently cast of gilt bronze. Monumental in size, this pair meant to hold seven candles is very complex in its design. Arranged in two tiers of three branches and with an additional arm at the top, the model incorporates two sets of animal feet as its support, lion's paws and goat's hooves. The stem is surmounted by female term figures, possibly maenads, and the scrolling branches on the lower tier each terminate in a jester's head, with a tambourine serving as drip pan (see detail above). In addition, eagle's heads and coiling snakes surround a marble vase topped with fruits and flowers, which supports the four upper branches. Vine leaves and bunches of grapes are entwined around three of the candle arms, while the upper one is shaped like a thyrsus, the staff associated with Bacchus. The selection of bronze ornaments is unusual, and attention has been lavished on their casting, chasing, and gilding, which is partly burnished and partly left matte.

DK-G

References: Watson 1969, p. 188, fig. 8; Francis J. B. Watson in Watson and Dauterman 1970, pp. 57–59, no. 299a, b, ill.; Penelope Hunter in Metropolitan Museum of Art 1975, p. 260, ill.

72. Pair of twenty-four-light chandeliers (*lustres*)

France, ca. 1790
Gilt bronze, rock crystal
H. 62 in. (157.5 cm), diam. 45 in. (114.3 cm)
Gift of Mr. and Mrs. Charles Wrightsman, 1971
(1971.206.40, 41)

Numerous entries in the account book for the period 1748–58 of the *marchand-mercier* Lazare Duvaux show that he not only sold, shipped, and installed chandeliers but also took them apart for cleaning or repairs and reassembled them afterward. At times Duvaux would also provide crystal drops, finials, and globes to replace missing ones or mend those that were broken. This may explain why the late eighteenth-century frames of this magnificent pair of chandeliers incorporate earlier crystal pendants in their design. Arranged in three tiers, rope-twisted candle arms alternate with inward-scrolling branches decorated with acanthus leaves, stylized seedpods, and crystal finials. The elaborate model further includes gilt-bronze chains with crystal beads as well as a profusion of crystal drops and balls raining down from the umbrella-shaped row of arms near the top and from the multiple branches below. The splendid impression such fixtures created when lit (see fig. 48) did not escape the baronne d'Oberkirch. Describing a concert held in May 1782, during the visit of Grand Duke Paul of Russia and his duchess, Maria Feodorovna, to Versailles, she noted particularly that "the palace was all brilliantly illuminated, as on days of high ceremonial. A thousand chandeliers were suspended from the ceil-

Fig. 48. View of the Louis XVI Gallery with the chandeliers in situ.

ings, and candelabra holding forty candles each were placed on top of the console tables. . . . Nothing can express this splendor and opulence."[1]

DK-G

1. Oberkirch 1789/1970, p. 156.

Reference: Francis J. B. Watson in Watson and Dauterman 1970, pp. 62–63, no. 302a, b, ill.

Chimneypieces and Fireplace Furnishings

DANIËLLE KISLUK-GROSHEIDE

The chimneypiece [in the Dressing Room] will be in veined white marble; its consoles will be rounded in plan, and the mantel will follow their contour. The top of the opening cannot be placed too low; and the view afforded by the glass over the mantel will be all the better if another is placed on the opposite wall. These repetitions are necessary, so that one may see oneself from every side.

—Nicolas Le Camus de Mézières, *Le Génie de l'architecture*

As it was the dominant architectural element in most rooms and framed the principal source of heat and light, the chimneypiece, or mantelpiece, received much attention during the seventeenth and eighteenth centuries. Architects included their ideas on the placement and decoration of this intrinsic part of domestic and public buildings in their treatises. Frequently positioned on a wall perpendicular to the windows, but sometimes also found between the windows in a room, the chimneypiece should always—according to the architect Nicolas Le Camus de Mézières (1721–1783)—be placed so as "not to impede persons walking from one room to another, especially in anterooms. The Domestic Servant is gross and uneducated, in general; it is pointless to lay him open to the consequences of his own carelessness."[1]

The size of the chimneypiece was determined by the dimensions of the space to be heated; its width should be about one-sixth of the room, and the height of the mantel, which was lowered considerably during the eighteenth century to reduce drafts, should be two-thirds of the width of the fireplace opening. Le Camus de Mézières added: "Have no fear of making mantels too low: a pressing argument is the resultant ease of seeing oneself in the glass above; the less high, the less the exposure to smoke."[2] Smoke-filled rooms were a real hazard, as is vividly illustrated by Horace Walpole's description of a Parisian ball

given by the second Earl of Massareene in January 1766: "The chimneys in that dirty *hôtel garni* smoked so much, that to save our eyes, we were forced to put out the fires and open the windows." As a result, Walpole continued, "half the candles were blown out, and the fingers of the violin[ist]s so frozen, that they missed every other note."[3]

During the seventeenth century the chimneypiece had been carved of wood or stone, but in the following century it was generally made of marble and consisted of two uprights supporting a frieze and the shelf of the mantel above. The choice of marble dictated what was used for the tops of console tables or commodes in the same room. Closely reflecting the evolution of style, the principal beauty of a mantelpiece relied not only on its shape but also on the relationship with the surrounding paneling, asserted Jacques-François Blondel (1705–1774) in his *Cours d'architecture* (1771–77).[4] The ornamentation depended on the function of the room: for less important spaces, such as antechambers, the decoration was kept simple, while in formal reception rooms it was more lavishly conceived, and often included gilt bronze. The Scottish architect Sir William Chambers (1723–1796) warned in his treatise of 1759 that "all nudities, and indecent representations, must be avoided in Chimney-Pieces; and indeed, in every other Ornament of Apartments, to which Children, Ladies, and other modest and grave persons, have constant recourse; together with all representations capable of exciting Horrour, Grief, Disgust, &c."[5] The French appear to have been less sensitive on this point, however (see no. 77). At times, the French fireplace was more beautiful than effective. After spending six years in Russia, the painter Marie-Louise-Élisabeth Vigée-Lebrun (1755–1842) returned to Paris in 1801, and there she visited the Princess Dolgoruki. In her memoirs, Vigée-Lebrun wrote that they "were both so cold in

Fig. 49. Pierre-Louis Dumesnil the Younger, *Interior with Card Players*, eighteenth century. Oil on canvas, 31⅛ × 38¾ in. (79.1 × 98.4 cm). The Metropolitan Museum of Art, New York, Bequest of Harry G. Sperling, 1971 (1976.100.8).

front of her fireplace that we said, 'We must go to spend the winter in Russia to get warm.'"[6]

The use of large plates of mirror glass on the overmantel increased the illumination in a room through the reflection of daylight or candlelight (see fig. 49). When a second mirror was placed on the wall opposite the chimneypiece, interesting perspective views were created, offering the suggestion of an infinite series of rooms. Blondel mentioned furthermore that the overmantel mirror gave people gathered around the fireplace the additional benefit of being able to observe who was entering or leaving the room without having to turn their heads.[7]

The mantel shelf became the repository for a so-called *garniture de cheminée*, consisting of multiple vases of porcelain. However, candelabra and a clock were also frequently displayed on the mantel. A pair of firedogs, or andirons—their uprights concealing the iron supports for the logs—stood inside the fireplace. Large and imposing during the seventeenth century, andirons became smaller during the following century, when they were generally made of gilt bronze. Gilt-bronze handles decorated the fire tongs and shovel that were held in place by brackets on either side of the mantelpiece, as can be seen in nearly all the Wrightsman rooms.

Epigraph. Le Camus de Mézières 1780/1992, p. 120.

1. Le Camus de Mézières 1780/1992, p. 107.
2. Ibid.
3. Horace Walpole to George Selwyn, January 12, 1766, in Walpole 1937–83, vol. 30 (1961), p. 211.
4. Blondel 1771–77, vol. 5 (1777), p. 67.
5. Chambers 1759, p. 79.
6. Vigée-Lebrun 1834–35/1904, p. 101.
7. Blondel 1771–77, vol. 5 (1777), p. 67.

73. Chimneypiece (*cheminée*)

France, ca. 1660–70
Carved limestone
H. 13 ft. 2 in. (4 m), w. 8 ft. 2 in. (2.49 m)
Gift of The Hearst Foundation, 1956 (56.234.34)

This monumental chimneypiece with its high opening and elaborately carved hood bears analogies to the work of the designer and engraver Jean Le Pautre (1618–1682). A prolific and versatile artist who worked for the Crown, Le Pautre created many designs in a bold sculptural manner, their subjects ranging from architectural elements such as ceilings and friezes to garden vases and trophies. Through his engraved work, he is credited with the dissemination of the Louis XIV style. One plate from his series entitled *Cheminées à la Romaine* (fig. 50) shows the basic design for the Museum's chimneypiece, which originated at the Château du Chay in Chérac, in the department of Charente-Maritime, on the French west coast. Closely related to Le Pautre's engraving are the youthful satyr figures above the hearth opening and the seated boys with olive branches who flank the central medallion. The identity of the helmeted young man in the medallion has not yet been established. Could he have been a member of the De Ferray du Chay family, who owned the castle during the seventeenth century, or is the image merely a classicizing bust? It has been suggested that the features bear a certain resemblance to those of the young

Fig. 50. *Design for a Chimney Piece*, from Jean Le Pautre, *Cheminées à la Romaine* (Paris, ca. 1663). Engraving. The Metropolitan Museum of Art, New York, Harris Brisbane Dick Fund, 1933 (33.84 [1]).

Louis XIV—which would explain the crown-bearing putto flying above.

Whatever the case may be, this chimneypiece, probably executed by a local master, illustrates beautifully how Le Pautre's designs served as a source of inspiration for artists working far away from the French court.

References: Raggio 1989, fig. 2; Meyer 1990, figs. 1, 2.

74. Pair of firedogs (*chenets*) in the form of Jupiter and Juno

Probably cast in France during the 18th century
after models by Alessandro Algardi (1598–1654)
Black-lacquered bronze
(.16) h. 45½ in. (115.6 cm); (.17) h. 44¼ in.
(112.4 cm)
Gift of Mr. and Mrs. Charles Wrightsman, 1973
(1973.315.16, 17)

According to the prominent biographer of artists Giovanni Pietro Bellori (1613–1696), the Baroque sculptor Alessandro Algardi, active in Rome, modeled a set of four firedogs representing the four elements in the guise of mythological figures. Commissioned for Philip IV, king of Spain, the models were created not long before the artist's death, in 1654. Two of the designs, the figures of Jupiter and Juno as fire and air—a symbolism quite appropriate to their use as firedogs—were executed on a reduced scale for the French court, both in silver and in bronze. Firedogs of this exuberant model, which create a sense of movement and are interesting in the round, also found a market among the French aristocracy and are listed in late seventeenth- and eighteenth-century inventories and sale catalogues. It is generally thought that some of them—varying slightly from Algardi's originals, which are still extant in Spain—were made in France rather than in Italy. The Museum's firedogs were cast in multiple pieces, which have been carefully joined together. They have largely kept their original patina.

The chief Roman god, Jupiter, ruler of the sky and master of lightning and thunder, is seated on an eagle, a form he once assumed, atop a globe. Two kneeling Titans shoulder the rocks on which the globe is poised, while a third reclines on the base. Facing her husband, the goddess Juno is perched on her own symbolic animal, the peacock. Representing beauty, this bird stands on a globe carried by wind gods, their cheeks full of air.

Although the casts have long been considered seventeenth century, the raised heads of the deities and the sweet, smiling countenance of Juno, as well as her hair ornament and details of her sandals, suggest an eighteenth-century date for the Museum's majestic firedogs instead.

References: Francis J. B. Watson in Fahy and Watson 1973, pp. 362–66, no. 43a, b, ill.; James David Draper in Metropolitan Museum of Art 1975, p. 247, ill.; Montagu 1985, vol. 2, p. 412, nos. 129.c.4, 130.c.4.

75. Pair of firedogs (*chenets*)

France, ca. 1750
Gilt bronze
(.1) h. 20¾ in. (52.8 cm), w. 19 in. (48.3 cm), d. 10½ in. (26.7 cm); (.2) h. 17¾ in. (45.1 cm), w. 19⁵⁄₁₆ in. (49.1 cm), d. 9¾ in. (24.8 cm)
Gift of Mrs. Charles Wrightsman, 1986
(1986.365.1, 2)

Multiple examples of this model of firedogs, incorporating the figures of two mythological deities in their design, are known. The crowned male figure could be Pluto, Roman god of the underworld; the female pendant might be his love, Proserpina, traditionally shown with a torch, as the woman is here. In fact, in 1753 the metalworker Antoine Lelièvre supplied a pair of *chenets* decorated with

the rulers of the underworld, albeit of a different model, to Louis XV for use at Versailles. However, Pluto is generally rendered with a scepter, not with a trident as here, the latter usually being an attribute of Neptune. Given the fact that andirons were placed in front of the fireplace to reflect the flames, the choice of Neptune and his spouse, Amphitrite, god and goddess of the sea, would have been an amusing one. Whatever their identities might be, these firedogs with their figures perched on pierced scrolling bases evolving into acanthus leaves are a perfect embodiment of the whimsical Rococo taste.

References: Watson 1966c, p. 377, no. 194a, b, ill.; Daniel Alcouffe in Alcouffe, Dion-Tenenbaum, and Mabille 2004, p. 67, under no. 27.

76. Pair of firedogs
(*chenets*)

Paris, ca. 1772
Quentin-Claude Pitoin (1725–1777)
Gilt bronze
(.5) h. 16 in. (40.6 cm), w. 24¼ in. (61.6 cm),
d. 7⅝ in. (19.4 cm); (.6) h. 15½ in. (39.4 cm),
w. 24¼ in. (61.6 cm), d. 7⅝ in. (19.4 cm)
Gift of Mr. and Mrs. Charles Wrightsman, 1977
(1977.102.5, 6)

Attributes of hunting embellish these
highly accomplished models, which are
known to have been repeated in different sizes. The small sculpture of a
wild boar on the left andiron and of a
reclining stag on the other surmount
a rectangular base, which is further
enriched with a relief panel in front
showing, below the boar, dead game
and, below the stag, a sleeping hound
amid game. Dogs' pelts, oak and ivy

branches, and a pile of additional game,
all beautifully chased and finished,
are also incorporated in the elaborate
designs. The figure of the boar at bay
is derived from a lifesize Roman
marble in the Galleria degli Uffizi, in
Florence. That antique sculpture was
reproduced in bronze, much reduced
in size, by the Florentine sculptor and
bronze caster Giovanni Francesco
Susini (1585–ca. 1653). One of his early

seventeenth-century replicas was probably the source for the sculptural boar on the Museum's andiron. Madame du Barry appears to have been the first to own a pair of firedogs of this model. They were delivered for use in her apartment at the royal hunting castle at Fontainebleau in October 1772 by Quentin-Claude Pitoin, principal supplier of *bronzes d'ameublement* to the court.

The Museum's andirons are believed to have been in the possession of the French statesman Charles Gravier, comte de Vergennes (1719–1787), who was sent as envoy to Trier and appointed ambassador to the Ottoman Empire and Sweden, and who later served as foreign minister under Louis XVI. The moving flames of a fire on the hearth, reflected in the differently worked surfaces of the

firedogs, would have brought the stag and the boar, albeit temporarily, to life.

References: Watson 1966c, pp. 382–85, no. 199a, b, ill.; Gérard Mabille in Alcouffe, Dion-Tenenbaum, and Mabille 2004, p. 120, under no. 55.

77. Chimneypiece (*cheminée*)

Paris, 1784
After a design by François-Joseph Bélanger (1744–1818); figures modeled by Jean-Joseph Foucou (1739–1815); bronzes by François Rémond (1747–1812)
Verde di Levanto marble; patinated bronze and gilt bronze
H. 45½ in. (115.7 cm), w. 5⅜ in. (186.5 cm), d. 17¾ in. (45.1 cm)
Gift of Mr. and Mrs. Charles Wrightsman, 1976 (1976.227)

77 (details)

The model of this imposing Neoclassical chimneypiece, incorporating large figures of female satyrs as supports of the architrave and mantel shelf, was repeated a number of times. Although commissioned for the Grand Salon Ovale of the Hôtel Thelusson in Paris, the chimneypiece appears never to have been installed there. It was used at the Hôtel de Massa instead, a residence rented by the banker Paul-Louis de Thelusson (b. ca. 1762) in January 1785. The earliest mantelpiece of this design appears to have been the one for the Paris *hôtel particulier* of Louise-Jeanne de Durfort, duchesse de Mazarin (1735–1781), for which Pierre Gouthière executed the bronzes in 1781. Made of blue turquin marble, that first mantelpiece is very well documented, and we therefore know that the architect François-Joseph Bélanger was responsible for its design and that the striking caryatid figures, their legs crossed and hands folded above their heads, were modeled by the sculptor Jean-Joseph Foucou. Gouthière was to supply five different mantelpieces for the Hôtel Thelusson but was able to finish the

work for only four of them. The bronze figures and decoration of the fifth were done by François Rémond in 1784, and it is believed to be the one now in the Museum's collection.

The bronze satyresses have a dark patination but their paraphernalia are gilded—the wreath of vine leaves and grapes in their hair, the drapery cascading down their backs, and the ivy girdle hiding their nudity. In addition, a gilded strap runs across the chests and a similar ribbon is tied around the hooves of these mythological half-figures, attendants of the wine god Bacchus. Musical instruments are suspended from the

straps—a pair of cymbals on the left and a tambourine on the right—and bells are attached to the ribbons; thus these satyresses could make music during their drunken revelry. The lustrous and sensuous skin of their upper bodies starkly contrasts with their hairy goat's legs. Unlike the other known examples of this design, the Museum's mantelpiece is the only one in which the frieze is entirely decorated with repeating gilt-bronze ornament.

References: Watson 1966c, pp. 518–21, no. 287, ill.; Baulez 1986, pp. 586–87, fig. 27; Dell 1992, pp. 124–33 (mentioned on p. 130).

Textiles and Leather

DANIËLLE KISLUK-GROSHEIDE

Furnishing textiles played a vital role in the interiors of the seventeenth and eighteenth centuries. Wall and bed hangings, upholstery materials, carpets, and window treatments not only provided a profusion of tones and textures and served as protection against drafts but could also create a lavish decor and offer a unified color scheme. A sense of the importance of the textile component of a room was given by Martin Lister when describing the residences of the "Persons of Distinction" in late seventeenth-century Paris: "As the Houses are magnificent without, so the Finishing within . . . and Furniture answer in Riches and Neatness[: they include] . . . Hangings of rich Tapestry, raised with Gold and Silver Threads, Crimson Damask and Velvet Beds or of Gold and Silver Tissue." [1]

In order to reduce imports and favorably compete with products made abroad, the French government strongly developed its textile industry during the reign of Louis XIV. Not only beautiful silks and velvets, taffetas, and brocades but also tapestries, carpets, and embroideries were created at the various workshops in Paris, Lyons, Tours, Beauvais, and other places (see figs. 51, 52).

Owing to the labor-intensive and time-consuming process of their manufacture, textiles—which, as Dr. Lister noted, sometimes had shimmering highlights in gold or silver—were among the most magnificent and costly of the interior furnishings. Unfortunately, those splendid materials often fell victim to changes in fashion or were ravaged by light, dust, and use. Both aspects—their expense and their fragile nature—were not lost on Gouverneur Morris, who wrote in 1789, after visiting the most renowned tapestry workshops in Paris: "First the Gobelins [manufactory], which after all that has been said in their Favor are I think an idle Kind of Art because they produce Pieces which are more costly and less beautiful than Paintings, and tho in one Sense they last long, yet in another they do not because the Colors fade. For the Rest it is a wonderful Operation." [2] Ironically, despite their delicate nature, the carpets and embroideries in the Wrightsman Galleries included in this section date to the second half of the seventeenth century and are therefore among the oldest works of art displayed there.

1. Lister 1699, pp. 8–9.
2. Morris 1789–93/1939, vol. 1, p. 99.

Fig. 51. *Weaving a Knotted-Pile Carpet*, plate IV in Henri-Louis Duhamel du Monceau, *Art de faire les tapis façon de Turquie* (Paris, 1766). The Metropolitan Museum of Art, New York, The Thomas J. Watson Library.

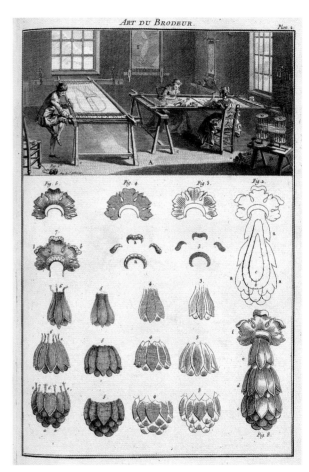

Fig. 52. *Embroidery Workshop*, plate II in Charles-Germain de Saint-Aubin, *L'Art du brodeur* (Paris, 1770). The Metropolitan Museum of Art, New York, The Thomas J. Watson Library.

78. Carpet (*tapis*)

Paris, mid-17th century
Knotted and cut wool pile, woven with about 44
knots per square inch
L. 12 ft. 2 in. (3.71 m), w. 8 ft. 4 in. (2.54 m)
Gift of Mr. and Mrs. Charles Wrightsman, 1976
(1976.155.111)

Until 1671 the manufactory known as Savonnerie occupied workshops not only at the Louvre but also at the site of a former soap factory at Chaillot—hence the name Savonnerie, from the French *savon*, or soap. Textiles created at both locations during the first half of the seventeenth century are generally known as Louis XIII carpets. They are small in size and display a wealth of floral ornament against a black ground. Despite their name, however, many of these exquisite rugs were actually woven early in the reign of Louis XIV, who nominally became king in 1643, a few months before his fifth birthday.

This well-preserved example in the Museum's collection may originally have been intended as a table carpet. Almost serving as a carpet within a carpet, the central field has a border edged with trompe l'oeil tassels that seem to hang down on all sides when the rug is placed on a rectangular table the size of the field. Decorating the central panel is a floral wreath enclosing a large bouquet, flanked at either narrow end by a stone pedestal on which a basket of flowers is placed. The outer border is embellished with bowls, baskets, and vases filled with fruit and flowers that

alternate with floral bouquets, echoing motifs seen in contemporary paintings. The bright colors used for the profusion of naturalistic flowers give the carpet a particularly fresh and lively appearance. Among them is the striped or flamed tulip; its bulb commanded high prices, resulting in a frenzy of speculation called tulipomania during the 1630s. The blue and white bowls reflect the fashion for Chinese porcelain, a prized commodity imported to Europe by ships of the East India Companies.

References: Watson 1966c, pp. 492–93, no. 276, ill.; Verlet 1982, pp. 81, 83, fig. 44; Sherrill 1996, pp. 68, 69, pl. 67.

79. Carpet (*tapis*)

Paris, third quarter of the 17th century
Knotted and cut wool pile, woven with about 90 knots per square inch
L. 21 ft. (6.4 m), w. 12 ft. (3.65 m)
Gift of Mr. and Mrs. Charles Wrightsman, 1976 (1976.155.113)

The initial goal of the Savonnerie manufactory was to imitate knotted-pile carpets from the Near East, which were much admired in Europe, but during Louis XIV's reign the workshop established its own style. The field of this particular carpet still shows a dependence on Persian designs in its use of differently shaped compartments that are linked by strapwork. In a fusion of traditions, the naturalistic blossoms that fill these medallions as well as the cream-colored ground between them are purely European in nature. The broad border has a dense floral pattern against a black ground, which includes vases, baskets, and bowls of flowers similar to those found on so-called Louis XIII carpets (see detail below). Among the depicted blooms are tulips and crown imperials, popular flowers that had been introduced to Western Europe from the Near East during the late sixteenth century.

That carpets were not always treated with respect is borne out by a remark of the British traveler and diarist Mary Berry (1763–1852). Describing a visit in 1802 to the Hôtel d'Elboeuf, the Parisian residence of Jean-Jacques-Régis de Cambacérès

(1753–1824), Second Consul and author of the Napoleonic Code, she noted some "beautiful carpets, to which one's attention was every minute disagreeably called by all the men indiscriminately spitting upon them."[1]

1. Berry 1783–1852/1866, vol. 2, p. 160.

Reference: Watson 1966c, pp. 490–91, no. 275, ill.

80. Carpet (*tapis*)

Paris, 1668–85
After designs by Charles Le Brun (1619–1690)
and Louis Le Vau (1612–1670)
Knotted and cut wool pile, woven with about 90
knots per square inch
L. 30 ft. (9.15 m), w. 15 ft. (4.57 m)
Gift of Samuel H. Kress Foundation, 1958
(58.75.129)

In his *A New Description of Paris*, of 1687, Germain Brice (1652–1727) mentioned work in progress on "a great Footcloth in the manner of Turky-work, . . . in a place built on purpose at the end of the *Cours de la Reine*, commonly called the *Savonnerie*, which is to be the full length of the great Gallery of the Louvre, but is not yet finisht."[1] Brice referred here to a set of ninety-three carpets, of different but related designs, that was being created for the Grande Galerie of the Palais du Louvre in Paris. The Savonnerie manufactory, which received a monopoly from Louis XIII in 1627 to make knotted-pile rugs in the manner of the Levant, experienced its most creative period under Louis XIV, when the workshops were placed under the direction of the king's First Painter, Charles Le Brun. The project to cover with carpets the entire floor of the long gallery at the Louvre, measuring more than 480 yards in length, was the most ambitious commission the Savonnerie ever received. The work space was expanded and extra-wide looms were created to accommodate this monumental task. Contrary to tradition, the size of the looms was based on the length of the carpets (which in turn was determined by the width of the long gallery). The individual designs of the series most likely reflected in some degree the decoration of the ceiling and walls of the gallery.

Set against a black ground with scrolling acanthus leaves in the corners, the main motifs of the Museum's splendid carpet, number thirty-eight of the series, are full of references to the monarchy. The sunflower, symbol of the Sun King, is flanked by the French royal arms and by Louis XIV's crowned monogram of interlaced Ls.

A number of the carpets for the Grande Galerie have compartments at either narrow end showing simulated bas-reliefs in grisaille representing different aspects and virtues of good government. Here the personifications of fame, blowing a trumpet, and fortitude, with a lion and a column, are depicted. Although all the carpets

of the original commission but one were woven between 1670 and 1689, Louis XIV appears to have lost interest in the interior decoration of the Louvre, and thus in this monumental project, when he focused his attention on Versailles instead, moving his court there in 1682. When Horace Walpole visited the Louvre in August

1771 the palace was in a derelict state. "Saw the great gallery of Le Brun with battles of Alexander, all the ornaments, ceiling, shutters and even locks and bolts designed by Le Brun, but so abominably neglected that it rains in."[2] Perhaps it was not such a bad thing after all that the series of Savonnerie carpets appears never to have been laid out in the Grande Galerie as originally intended.

1. Brice 1687, p. 14.
2. Journal entry for August 24, 1771, in Walpole 1937–83, vol. 7 (1939), p. 339.

References: Parker 1960a, pp. 307–8, fig. 43; Edith Appleton Standen in Dauterman, Parker, and Standen 1964, pp. 247–50, no. 60, figs. 210–13; Jarry 1966, p. 29, fig. 16.

81–84. Four embroidered hangings (*tentures brodées*)

France, probably Paris, ca. 1684–85
Designs for the central figures probably by the workshop of Charles Le Brun (1619–1690); designs for the decorative borders attributed to Jean Lemoyen le Lorrain (1637/38–1709)
Silk, wool, and metal thread on canvas; designs embroidered in tent stitch (*petit point*), backgrounds in couched silver and silver-gilt thread in herringbone and spiral patterns
(.1) h. 13 ft. 8 in. (4.17 m), w. 9 ft. (2.74 m);
(.2) h. 14 ft. 6 in. (4.42 m), w. 9 ft. 2 in. (2.79 m);
(.3) h. 14 ft. (4.27 m), w. 9 ft. 1 in. (2.77 m);
(.4) h. 14 ft. (4.27 m), w. 9 ft. (2.74 m)
Rogers Fund, 1946 (46.43.1–4)

Representing spring and summer, fire and air, these hangings were part of a larger set that must also have included the two missing seasons and elements. This series included portraits of Louis XIV, his mistress Françoise-Athénaïs de Rochechouart, marquise

de Montespan (1641–1707), and six of their children, all shown as deities. The hangings were probably worked at the convent of the Filles de Saint-Joseph in Paris, which was under the patronage of Madame de Montespan, and where she retired in 1691. At this religious community, orphan girls were educated in the art of needlepoint, and a number of royal embroidery projects for use at Versailles were executed there, with the additional assistance of professional embroiderers. The Museum's four panels are believed to have been commissioned by Madame de Montespan about the time the king transferred his affections from her to Françoise d'Aubigny, marquise de Maintenon (1635–1719), whom he was to marry in 1685.

The central medallion in the panel that symbolizes air (no. 84) features the king himself in the guise of Jupiter, holding a thunderbolt and a shield emblazoned with the head of the Gorgon Medusa and seated on a large eagle against a backdrop of billowing clouds. Various birds, insects, and wind instruments are rendered around this medallion, while a sunburst is shown above and Juno with peacock below. The closeness of the depiction of Louis XIV to an image of the king painted on the ceiling of the Hall of Mirrors at Versailles by Charles Le Brun in 1683–84 makes it likely that the designs for the main figures in the set of hangings were supplied by his workshop; however, they may be the work of the painter François Bonnemer (1638–1689), who is known to have made cartoons after compositions by Le Brun. In 1685 Bonnemer provided designs for

the embroidered seat covers of the benches and stools in the Hall of Mirrors at Versailles. The *alentours*, or decorative borders, full of delightful details, are believed to be by Jean Lemoyen le Lorrain, an artist little known today who worked in the circle of Le Brun.

The other embroideries are thought to depict three of Montespan's children with the king: Louise-Françoise, Mademoiselle de Nantes (1673–1743), with flowers symbolizing Flora, or spring (no. 81); Françoise-Marie, Mademoiselle de Blois (1677–1749), with wheat ears, as Ceres, or summer (no. 82); and Louis-Auguste, duc de Maine (1670–1736), in armor, as Mars, or fire (no. 83).

The compositions of the seasons include floral wreaths with the zodiac symbols for the appropriate months, while salamanders, torches, smoking braziers, and censers pertain to the element fire. The background of these rare surviving embroideries is worked in metal thread, now tarnished, which must have given them a sumptuous and shimmering appearance when they were first made. The hangings were documented in 1718 as in the collection of Louis-Alexandre, comte de Toulouse (1678–1737), the youngest child of Louis XIV and Madame de Montespan, at the Château de Rambouillet. During the nineteenth century they belonged to King Louis-Philippe and were hung at the Palais Royal, Paris.

References: Standen 1951, ill.; Standen 1985, vol. 2, pp. 665–76, no. 117, ill.; Alice M. Zrebiec in Parker et al. 1989, pp. 32–33, 64, ill.; Véron-Denise 2005, figs. 3–6; Bremer-David forthcoming.

81 *Spring*

82 *Summer*

83 *Fire*

84 *Air*

85. Briefcase (*portefeuille*)

Turkey and France, ca. 1763–64
Case: probably Constantinople
Morocco leather embroidered with gold thread
and silk thread; silk lining
H. 13⅛ in. (33.3 cm), w. 17¾ in. (45 cm),
d. 2½ in. (6.3 cm)
Lock: probably by the Parisian goldsmith Jacques
Lourdière (master in 1746–after 1768)
Gold
Gift of Mrs. Charles Wrightsman, 2001
(2001.653)

Made in Turkey for the western market, morocco leather briefcases were
fashionable in both England and
France during the last quarter of the
seventeenth and throughout the eighteenth century. This sumptuous example embellished with embroidery in
silk and metal thread can be dated to
1763–64 by one of the marks on the
gold lock: the crowned letter *Z*, the
assay mark warranting the standard of
the metal.

The embroidery on the back dis-
plays both a banderole with the words
"Ministère des Affaires Étrangères"
(Ministry of Foreign Affairs) and the

coat of arms of César-Gabriel, comte
de Choiseul-Chevigny and later duc de
Praslin (1712–1785). This nobleman
enjoyed a successful military career
before undertaking a political one. He
served as foreign minister of France
from 1761 to 1766 and in that capacity
signed the Treaty of Paris, ending the
Seven Years' War, which for France
entailed the loss of much of her North
American territories to Great Britain.
Nevertheless, it is likely that the briefcase was intended to commemorate
this event, and perhaps also to celebrate the politician's elevation to the
rank of duke, which occurred in
October 1762 (the ducal crown forms
a prominent part of the coat of arms).

In his memoirs, Jean-Nicolas,
comte Dufort de Cheverny (1731–
1802), noted that the duc de Praslin
was cold and disagreeable, yet had a
passion for literature and found
happiness with his mistress, Marie-
Anne Botot, known as Mademoiselle
Dangeville (1714–1796), who was

famed for her roles as lady's maid at
the Comédie Française.[1]

Praslin, a bibliophile as well as a
collector of old-master paintings, had
only a few years to enjoy the use of his
briefcase. Following his resignation as
foreign minister, he was appointed to
the Ministry of the Navy but was dis-
missed by Louis XV four years later.

The preparation of the leather and
the embroidery of the portfolio may
have been done in Constantinople,
since there are several similar examples
known that bear the name of that city.
It was probably lined and finished in
Paris, where the escutcheon-shaped,
openwork lock was made as well.

1. Dufort de Cheverny 1794–95/1990,
   pp. 271, 482, n. 204.

References: *France in the Eighteenth Century*
1968, p. 147, no. 882, figs. 396, 397; Francis
J. B. Watson in Watson and Dauterman 1970,
pp. 271–75, no. 73, ill.; Daniel Alcouffe in
Louis XV 1974, pp. 400–401, no. 550, ill.

Portraits

DANIËLLE KISLUK-GROSHEIDE

I went first to Saint-Cloud to see my grandchildren, and I thought my little grandson so beautiful that I begged my son to have his portrait painted. When I receive one I shall send you a copy.

—Élisabeth-Charlotte, duchesse d'Orléans, to her aunt Sophia,
   Duchess of Hanover, August 28, 1704

Writing in 1708, Roger de Piles observed: "If painting be an imitation of nature, 'tis doubly so in a portrait; which not only represents a man in general, but such an one as may be distinguished from all others. And as the greatest perfection of a portrait is extreme likeness, so the greatest of its faults is to resemble a person for whom it was not made; since there are not in the world two persons quite like one another."[1] De Piles (1635–1709) was writing about painting, but the same could have been said about portraits made in clay or stone. Despite the fact that contemporary theorists thought portraiture less noble than history painting, there was a considerable demand for portraits in eighteenth-century France, and the works of celebrated portrait painters like Hyacinthe Rigaud (1659–1743) or Marie-Louise-Élisabeth Vigée-Lebrun were much sought after. Painted likenesses could range in format from busts to full-length depictions and in type from official representations in traditional poses to informal renderings in intimate settings. Made to commemorate or immortalize royals, aristocrats, dignitaries, and contemporary or historic notables such as philosophers, artists, and military heroes, or to memorialize and honor loved ones, portraits were also commissioned for political purposes or to glorify the sitter. They frequently served as gifts, and it was not uncommon to replicate them.

De Piles also stated that "likeness being the essence of portraiture, it would seem, that we ought to imitate defects as well as beauties, since by this means the imitation will be more complete,"[2] but artists regularly improved upon or idealized facial features to please their sitters. This is well illustrated by a remark that Emperor Joseph II made in 1777 during a visit to his sister Marie-Antoinette. Stopping "at the house of Mr. Le Moine [Jean-Baptiste Lemoyne; see entry no. 88], one of the best statuaries in Europe," the emperor saw a bust of Louis XV's mistress, the comtesse du Barry, and asked if "it was like her, and not too flattering."[3] Whether rendered with fidelity or with nature's shortcomings perfected, successful portraits not only document the physiognomy of historical figures for posterity but convey a sense of their personality as well. A good example of one that strikes a fine balance is the handsome marble medallion portraying Louis XVI (fig. 53) by the sculptor Philippe-Laurent Roland (1746–1816). Signed and dated 1787, this roundel was commissioned for the Drapers' Hall in Paris, honoring the king during whose reign the twelfth-century edifice was restored.

Paintings were generally not hung on *boiseries*; in their carved and gilded frames, following the latest fashion, they were usually arranged against colorful silk damask hangings (see fig. 47). Family and intimate portraits would find a place in the private apartments of a hôtel or palace, whereas formal renderings and royal busts were prominently displayed in public spaces, especially if they had been a gift from the ruler himself (as were, for example, nos. 86 and 88).

Epigraph. Orléans 1661–1722/1924–25, vol. 1, p. 238.

1. De Piles 1743, p. 158.
2. Ibid., p. 163.
3. Du Coudray 1778, p. 64.

Fig. 53. Philippe-Laurent Roland, *Louis XVI*, 1787. Marble medallion, diam. 27⅝ in. (70 cm); gilt and marble-ized wood frame, 59½ × 62¼ in. (151 × 158 cm). The Metropolitan Museum of Art, New York, Wrightsman Fund, 1990 (1990.234).

86. *Louis XV (1710–1774) as a Child*

Paris, ca. 1716–21
Hyacinthe Rigaud (1659–1743)
Oil on canvas
77 × 55½ in. (195.6 × 141 cm)
Purchase, Mary Wetmore Shively Bequest, in
memory of her husband, Henry L. Shively M.D.,
1960 (60.6)

In 1715 Hyacinthe Rigaud, the leading portraitist of the French court, was commissioned to paint an official portrait of the young Louis XV, who had succeeded his great-grandfather Louis XIV that year at the age of five. Seated on the throne, the young monarch is depicted in an ermine-lined blue velvet coronation robe, which cascades down behind him. Gold fleurs-de-lis, the symbol of the French monarchy, are embroidered on the robe and also embellish the upholstery of the throne and the cushion on which the king rests his foot. Wearing a chain with the Order of the Holy Spirit around his neck, Louis XV gestures with his left hand and holds a scepter in his right, while the other royal regalia are placed beside him. Billowing crimson drapery serves as a canopy for the young monarch in this formal representation. The original portrait by Rigaud, now at the Château de Versailles, is signed and dated September 1715. The Museum's painting is one of multiple versions that were ordered for Versailles by Philippe II, duc d'Orléans (1674–1723), who served as regent of France during Louis's minority. The carved inscription in the medallion of the contemporary frame states that this example was given by the king to Nicolas Ravot d'Ombreval (1680–1729) in 1724, the year the recipient was appointed lieutenant general of the Paris police.

Although Rigaud has portrayed him as His Majesty, King of France, Louis was nothing more than a small and sometimes naughty boy, as the mother of the regent, Élisabeth-Charlotte, duchesse d'Orléans, revealed in a letter to her half-sister Luise von Degenfeld (1661–1733), dated November 13, 1717: "The little King has a pretty figure and plenty of intelligence, but he is an ill-natured child who only loves his old governess and no one else in the world. He takes a dislike to people without reason, and loves making cutting remarks. I am not at all in his good books, but I take no notice, as by the time he is on the throne I shall no longer be in the world, and shan't be dependent on his whims."[1]

1. Orléans 1672–1722/1970, pp. 188–89.

References: Zafran 1983, p. 84, under no. 26, fig. III.2; Constans 1995, vol. 2, p. 755.

87. *Madame de Pompadour (1721–1764)*

Paris, 1748–51
Jean-Baptiste Pigalle (1714–1785)
Marble
H. 29½ in. (74.9 cm)
The Jules Bache Collection, 1949 (49.7.70)

This graceful bust of Madame de Pompadour, with her perfectly oval face, slender neck, and lovely shoulders, was completed by Jean-Baptiste Pigalle early in 1751. The bust was mentioned in *Nouvelles Littéraires* on January 21 that same year by the philosopher and obviously well-informed observer Guillaume-Thomas-François Raynal (1713–1796), known as Abbé Raynal: "Pigalle, our first sculptor after Bouchardon, . . . has just finished a bust of Mme de Pompadour. Its design is not perfect, but the head is admirable and the treatment of the flesh outstanding. Our country is very pleased with this piece, for it is the first time that French marble has been used for a work of this kind. Until now sculptors have used Italian marble." [1] In order to make French sculptors less dependent on Italian Carrara marble, the French government had recently established a quarry at Sost, in the Pyrenees, and one of the first blocks of the grayish white stone was supplied to Pigalle for the bust of the king's young mistress. The artist found it very difficult to carve, as it was both hard and brittle and kept flaking under his chisel. Nevertheless, he succeeded beautifully in creating a faithful likeness. With the head turned sideways to show off the marquise's pretty features and curly hair braided at the back and embellished with flowers on top, and with one breast exposed, the portrait also suggests the favorite's transparent skin. The garments discreetly identify the sitter: Madame de Pompadour's crowned monogram is worked into the lace ruffle (see detail below), while a clasp gathering the drapery on her left arm is decorated with three turrets, the main charge of her coat of arms.

The history of this bust is well documented. It was listed among the marquise's possessions following her death and was kept by her brother and heir, Abel-François Poisson de Vandières, marquis de Marigny (1727–1781). The portrait remained in French noble collections throughout

Detail of the carved lace showing the crowned monogram

176

the nineteenth century, before being sold to the American banker Jules S. Bache (1861–1944). The Parisian art dealer René Gimpel (1881–1945) recalled in his diary on September 3, 1919: "Looking through my accounts, I saw that I sold the bust of the Marquise de Pompadour . . . to Jules Bache of New York for $160,000."[2] His estate gave it to the Museum in 1949.

1. Quoted in Raggio 1967, p. 222.
2. Gimpel 1918–39/1963, p. 111.

References: Wildenstein 1915–17, ill.; Raggio 1967, pp. 222–29, figs. 7–10; Raggio 1991, pp. 242–43, fig. 22.

hunting with the king, gave a vivid description of him: "Lewis XV. . . . has large, full, prominent, black, piercing eyes, and a Roman nose. Upon the whole, his countenance betrays a handsome goodliness, and is certainly the remains of a manly beautifulness. His person is of a middle stature, rather too bulky for a young man. . . . He is extremely fond of women; nor has any man been more indulged that way. He is also fonder of wine than is the present fashion of France. He finds the saddle the seat of health, and spends more of

the day on it than off. He is particularly addicted to asking trifling questions, such as, How old are you? Or to say, You are seventy; you can't live long; and the like. In short, Lewis XV. is neither that wit his flatterers represent him, nor has he that weakness which his own countenance sometimes bespeak[s]."[2]

As favorite portraitist of Louis XV, Lemoyne was able to observe Louis directly, and he faithfully carved his likeness in marble. With noble features and softening flesh, the royal image expresses both grandeur and

88. *Louis XV (1710–1774)*

Paris, 1757
Jean-Baptiste Lemoyne (1704–1778)
Marble
H. 34¼ in. (87 cm)
Gift of George Blumenthal, 1941 (41.100.244)

On December 10, 1757, the *marchand-mercier* Lazare Duvaux charged Madame de Pompadour for the transportation of a marble bust of the king to Champs-sur-Marne, where Louis XV's former favorite had rented a château.[1] The entry in Duvaux's account book does not identify the sculptor of the bust, but it is believed to be the Museum's portrait by Jean-Baptiste Lemoyne, signed by the artist and dated the same year. Dressed in armor, his left shoulder covered by a flowing mantle, and wearing the Orders of the Holy Spirit and the Golden Fleece, the monarch is shown at the age of forty-seven. The British captain Philip Thicknesse, who went

pride, yet at the same time it exudes the king's love for life's pleasures so frankly described by Thicknesse. Made for Madame de Pompadour, the bust was bought from her estate by the monarch himself and later presented to Charles-François de Laverdy (1723–1793), his controller general of finances.

1. Duvaux 1748–58/1965, vol. 2, p. 340.
2. Thicknesse 1768, pp. 215–16.

References: Rubinstein-Bloch 1930, pl. XLV; Raggio 1967, pp. 221–22, figs. 1, 3, 4; *Masterpieces of Fifty Centuries* 1970, p. 278, no. 312, ill.

89. *Maria Luisa of Parma (1751–1819), Later Queen of Spain*

French, 1765
Laurent Pécheux (1729–1821)
Oil on canvas
90⅞ × 64¼ in. (230.8 × 164.5 cm)
Bequest of Annie C. Kane, 1926 (26.260.9)

Born in Lyons, Laurent Pécheux studied in Rome and was summoned from there to Parma in January 1765. He was to paint a likeness of the fourteen-year-old Maria Luisa, intended as a gift to the Spanish court. In his diary the artist recorded how the graceful and spirited young princess received him with great affability but complained about the boredom that she had already endured a number of times when sitting for her portrait. Despite this hardship, no one had yet managed to paint an accurate likeness. Nevertheless Maria Luisa, who was the granddaughter of both Louis XV of France and Philip V of Spain, was hopeful that Pécheux would succeed.

It is not known if the princess was pleased with this full-length rendering, which the painter, despite many distractions and much to the surprise of the court, was able to finish after forty days of work. Dressed in a formal gown of striped floral brocade, worn with corset and panniers to exaggerate her natural silhouette, the young lady is depicted in one of the interiors of the Palazzo Ducale. The artist has painted with great precision the Turkish Ushak carpet, the velvet pillow, and the armchair, one of a set acquired by the sitter's mother in Paris in 1749 (see no. 18), as well as the French elephant clock on the gilded console table. Posing with a closed fan in her left hand, Maria Luisa holds in the other an enameled and bejeweled gold snuffbox. In all likelihood this precious box was a gift of her cousin and fiancé, Prince of Asturias, the future Charles IV of Spain (1748–1819), whose miniature is visible inside the opened lid.

References: Bollea 1942, pp. 41–43, 372–75, 394, no. 24; Parker 1966, pp. 182–86, fig. 2.

90. *Denis Diderot (1713–1784)*

Paris, 1773
Jean-Antoine Houdon (1741–1828)
Marble
Bust h. 15¾ (40 cm); base h. 4⅝ in. (11.8 cm)
Gift of Mr. and Mrs. Charles Wrightsman, 1974
(1974.291)

A philosopher and man of letters, and one of the internationally famous exponents of the French Enlightenment, Denis Diderot is best known for the multivolume encyclopedia that he compiled and coedited with Jean Le Rond d'Alembert (1717–1783) between 1751 and 1772. In the entry for painted portraits, Diderot's *Encyclopédie* states that the principal merit of the genre is to render the sitter exactly, by capturing both his character and his physiognomy.[1] A portrait bust of Diderot, believed to be the terracotta bust now in the Musée du Louvre, which served as a model for the Museum's marble version, was exhibited by the sculptor Jean-Antoine Houdon at the Salon of 1771. The sitter approved of that work, describing it as *très ressemblant* (having a very strong resemblance). It was also well received by contemporary critics, one of whom wrote: "I single out the bald head of the editor of the *Encyclopédie*. The flame of genius brought that bust to life; there is a fire, an expression, that gives it a striking resemblance; I don't want to say it out loud, but our colleagues the painters have done nothing equal."[2]

Winner of the Prix de Rome in 1761, Houdon had spent ten years in Italy and was profoundly influenced by the arts of antiquity. Diderot is shown as a classical philosopher, bare-chested and without wig or other paraphernalia. Justly known for his naturalistic portraiture and his classic simplicity, Houdon was very successful in capturing his sitter's lively eyes and conveying the determination and intelligence that won Diderot many admirers and some enemies—as attested by the words inscribed on the plinth: "il eut de grands Amis et, quelques bas jaloux / le Soleil plait à l'aigle, et blesse les hiboux" (He had great friends and a few low jealous ones / the sun pleases the eagle and wounds the owls). The slightly parted lips are said to have suggested the brilliance of Diderot's conversation. This is consistent with Horace Walpole's description of the philosopher in his journal entry for September 19, 1765, as "a very lively old man, and great talker."[3]

Possibly shown at the Salon of 1773, the Museum's marble bust, signed and dated by the artist, was acquired by a patron of Houdon's, the Russian Francophile Count Alexander Sergeyevich Stroganoff (1733–1811), during a sojourn in Paris. It remained for many years at the Stroganoff palace in Saint Petersburg. In 1773 Diderot himself traveled to Russia, at the invitation of Empress Catherine the Great (1729–1796), a supporter of his work with whom he had corresponded.

1. Diderot 1751–72, vol. 13 (1765), p. 153.
2. *Journal encyclopédique* (Collection Deloynes 49, no. 1320), quoted by Scherf 2008b, p. 44.
3. Walpole 1937–83, vol. 7 (1939), p. 262.

References: Francis J. B. Watson in Fahy and Watson 1973, pp. 398–405, no. 50, ill.; Hecht 1994, figs. 1, 2; Scherf 2008b, pp. 44, 164, under nos. 8, 9.

91. *Self-Portrait*

Paris, ca. 1785
Philippe-Laurent Roland (1746–1816)
Marble
Bust h. 16 in. (40.6 cm); base h. 4¾ in. (12.1 cm)
Purchase, The Annenberg Foundation Gift, in honor of Mrs. Charles Wrightsman, 1998 (1998.64)

Neither signed nor dated, this marble bust of a man with a bare chest is a self-portrait of the Neoclassical sculptor Philippe-Laurent Roland. The subject's profile matches that in a medallion of Roland executed by his pupil Pierre-Jean David d'Angers (1788–1856). Furthermore, the bust remained in the possession of members of the Roland family. Dating to about 1785, when the sculptor was nearly forty years of age and at the height of his powers, the portrait, though austere, shows a lean man with intelligent, well-knit features and a direct gaze. David d'Angers, who wrote a biography of his teacher, remembered Roland as a man of average height and with a high-strung

disposition: His "ruddy complexion revealed a sanguine character but with a predominantly nervous aspect. . . . His eyes were lively and penetrating like those of an artist. His mouth was large but well delineated. Like people occupied with serious matters, he spoke little. In his social relations he showed a dignified reserve and loyal sincerity which heightened his great austerity of principle."[1]

Roland had been a student of Augustin Pajou (1730–1809), a strong influence, who encouraged him to specialize in marble carving. As a portraitist, Roland is admired for the naturalistic, sympathetic rendering of his subjects in an advanced Neoclassical style, as is evident in the Museum's self-portrait.

1. Quoted in Jouin 1878, vol. 2, p. 243.

References: Baillio 1989, pp. 35–36, no. 26, ill.; James David Draper in "Recent Acquisitions" 1998, p. 38, ill.; Draper 1999, p. 542, figs. 9–11.

92. *Self-Portrait with a Harp*

France, ca. 1790
Rose-Adélaïde Ducreux (1761–1802)
Oil on canvas
76 × 50¼ in. (193 × 128.9 cm)
Bequest of Susan Dwight Bliss, 1966 (67.55.1)

In her memoirs, baronne d'Oberkirch noted that on May 31, 1782, she met at supper a young lady, Mademoiselle Sicard, who played the harp well. "This instrument was just then coming very much into fashion, and many ladies take advantage of it to display their lovely arms, and beautiful feet, to show off all their charm."[1] It was apparently not lost on painters either that the harp offered them the opportunity to portray female subjects in an attractive standing pose and at the same time allude to their musicality.

With a tuning hammer in her right hand, Rose Ducreux chose to represent herself testing the pitch of her harp, thus emphasizing her talents as a musician rather than as a painter. The daughter of the pastelist Joseph Ducreux (1735–1802), the artist was one of the successful women painters, like the better-known Marie-Louise-Élisabeth Vigée-Lebrun or Adélaïde Labille-Guiard, active during the late eighteenth century. Together with her father, she exhibited at the official Salon of 1791, the first time that this venue was open to nonacademicians, where this self-portrait was shown. The work was favorably commented on by contemporaries, who admired the graceful posture of the painter-model and the truthful depiction of the fabrics. Ducreux, who also painted miniatures, has shown great attention to detail in this painting, which is considered to be the finest known example of her work. Particularly beautiful is the rendering of the powdered curls, the folds in the striped gown, and the highlights in the shimmering satin of the bodice and skirt trimmed with a fringe. The book of sheet music on the table behind the instrument is open to an as yet unidentified love song by the harpist-composer Jean-Joseph-Benoît Pollet (1753–1818).

1. Oberkirch 1789/1970, p. 181.

Reference: Baillio 1988, pp. 23, 25, fig. 2.

Vincennes and Sèvres Porcelain

Jeffrey Munger

The Sèvres porcelain factory had its origins in a small workshop at the Château de Vincennes, located southeast of Paris. Experiments in the production of porcelain began there in 1740, and by about 1745 the small enterprise was producing its first examples of soft-paste porcelain, a variant of true porcelain, which is also known as hard-paste. The formula for hard-paste porcelain had not been discovered in France at this date, but the soft paste developed at Vincennes approximated the very white clay body that is a distinguishing feature of true porcelain. The young factory soon received a royal privilege, which gave it a distinct advantage over its French rivals, as well as the financial backing of Louis XV, who played an increasingly important role in the factory before finally acquiring it outright in 1759.

By 1753 the factory's commercial success made it apparent that larger quarters were needed, so three years later the factory moved to a new site, at Sèvres, to the west of the capital. With the support and patronage of Louis XV and his mistress, Madame de Pompadour, the Sèvres factory flourished. Highly talented French artists were hired to provide models and designs for the modelers and painters, and the specialization of skills encouraged by the directors produced superb results. By the late 1750s, the factory's products were setting the fashion for most of the other European porcelain manufactories, and its vases, dinner services, and other wares were avidly

Fig 54. *Sèvres Gilder*, late eighteenth century. Drawing, $7\frac{5}{8} \times 9\frac{5}{8}$ in. (19.5 × 24.4 cm). Archives, Manufacture Nationale de Sèvres (MNS, 0.731).

acquired by the French court, members of the landed aristocracy, and foreign visitors to Paris.

The Sèvres factory enjoyed great artistic success until the French Revolution, in large part because it sought to innovate constantly, creating new models and types of decoration that kept it in the forefront of fashion. The useful and decorative objects produced at Sèvres did much to make French artistic taste dominant in Europe, and they have helped shape our concept of French art and luxury in the eighteenth century.

93. Figure group representing Europe and America

Vincennes, ca. 1752
Soft-paste porcelain
H. 12½ in. (31.8 cm), w. 10⅝ in. (27 cm),
d. 6⅞ in. (17.5 cm)
Gift of Estate of James Hazen Hyde, 1959
(59.208.9)

A very limited number of figures and figure groups were made at the Vincennes porcelain factory; it was only after the move to a larger building at Sèvres in 1756 that the factory produced figures on a significant scale. This group with the personifications of Europe and America was made with a pendant, which represents the continents of Asia and Africa. In the present composition, Europe is depicted wearing a crown and reclining against her horse, with flags and a cornucopia at her feet. America, in a feathered headdress and skirt, holds a bow with a quiver of arrows and has a crocodile at her back. In the eighteenth century, these various attributes would have made the two continents to which they allude immediately identifiable. The vast majority of the figures first produced at Vincennes were not decorated with enamels but were only glazed. Perhaps because glaze was found to obscure the details of the modeling, it was used very rarely on figures after 1752. Examples produced after this date customarily were left unglazed, in the so-called biscuit state, in which the fired white porcelain resembles marble. The greater popularity of biscuit figures coincided with the developing Neoclassical taste, which held the marble sculpture of antiquity in especially high regard.

94. Vase (*urne Duplessis*)

Vincennes, ca. 1752
Model attributed to Jean-Claude Duplessis (active 1748–74)
Soft-paste porcelain
H. 9½ in. (24.1 cm), w. 5 in. (12.7 cm), d. 4⅜ in. (11.1 cm)
Gift of Mrs. Morris Hawkes, 1924 (24.214.4)

Some of the very earliest products of the Vincennes factory were in the style of Meissen, which was the dominant porcelain factory in Europe in the first half of the eighteenth cen-

tury. However, the new enterprise quickly developed its own recognizable style, which was entirely French in character, accomplishing this by hiring artists of high caliber who were already working in an established, distinctively French manner, and thus less susceptible to influence from Meissen.

This vase was designed by Jean-Claude Duplessis, the head of the modeling workshop at Vincennes and then at Sèvres, to which the factory moved in 1756. Duplessis had been

trained as a goldsmith, bronze worker, and sculptor, and his sculptural approach is evident in the many models he designed for manufacture in porcelain. This vase has been given a base in the form of molded rock work; the baluster shape is encrusted with three-dimensional flowers; and the handles are formed as two intertwined branches with clinging morning glories. In its use of motifs from nature, in the asymmetrical application of flowers, and in the sense of movement embodied by the design, the vase is a quintessential expression of the French Rococo style. The painted decoration is notable for being especially skillfully integrated with the three-dimensional flowers, which merge seamlessly with the two-dimensional ones.

95. Covered broth bowl and stand
(*écuelle ronde et plateau rond*)

Vincennes, ca. 1752–53
Soft-paste porcelain
Bowl h. 5⅛ in. (13 cm), w. 8½ in. (21.6 cm); stand diam. 8½ in. (21.6 cm)
Gift of R. Thornton Wilson, in memory of Florence Ellsworth Wilson, 1950
(50.211.168a,b, 169)

The extraordinary quality of the painting on this covered bowl and stand mark it as one of the exceptional objects produced at the Vincennes factory. The painted decoration includes numerous marine creatures portrayed in small vignettes that prominently include large-scale shells and vegetation. The enamel painting is executed with a degree of skill, sense of animation, and compositional sophistication that have few parallels in the Vincennes production. It is enhanced by the gilt highlights, which have been subtly incorporated throughout. It is very likely that the painter was working from print sources as yet unidentified, but the influence of the great Rococo artist and designer Juste-Aurèle Meissonnier has been suggested in regard to the painted scenes. These vignettes reflect the Rococo style at its apex, seen most noticeably in the asymmetrical compositions and in the prominent use of shells, one of the basic motifs of Rococo decoration.

As is noted in the entry for no. 110, covered bowls such as this were called

Detail of the bowl cover

Detail of the bowl

écuelles and were intended to contain broth or soup. Throughout much of the eighteenth century, broth was the preferred morning beverage and was served during the morning toilette, while one was being washed and groomed. These covered bowls, with an accompanying stand, were made for individual use and rarely as part of a larger service. On this *écuelle*, the finial in the form of a fish with shells beneath may have signaled that the contents were intended to be a type of fish broth.

Reference: Préaud and d'Albis 1991, pp. 150–51, no. 115 and frontispiece.

96. Pair of wine-bottle coolers (*seau à bouteille*)

Vincennes, 1753
Model attributed to Jean-Claude Duplessis
(active 1748–74)
Soft-paste porcelain
H. 7¾ in. (19.7 cm), w. 10¼ in. (26 cm), diam.
8 in. (20.3 cm)
Gift of Mr. and Mrs. Charles Wrightsman, 1970
(1970.230.4, 5)

These wine-bottle coolers are among the eight produced for one of the most famous porcelain services of the eighteenth century. The dinner and dessert service was ordered by Louis XV from the Vincennes factory in 1751, and it was delivered between 1753 and 1755, in three major installments because of the large number of pieces involved. The service included many new forms, and, most notably, it was

the first time that the ground color *bleu céleste* (sky blue) was employed for a service. This brilliant turquoise blue was one of the most expensive of all ground colors to produce, and it remained popular throughout the eighteenth century. The technical difficulty in achieving a uniform application of any ground color is evident in the slightly mottled aspect of the *bleu céleste* of these coolers, but the factory learned to overcome this obstacle several years after this service was made.

Many of the forms, or models, made for the service remained in production throughout the century, as it was prohibitively expensive to design new ones each time a service was

ordered. This model of wine-bottle cooler was designed by Jean-Claude Duplessis, director of the modeling workshop at the factory, who was responsible for the majority of the shapes produced at Vincennes and at its successor factory at Sèvres through the 1750s. It is not known which painters at the factory were responsible for the superb vignettes of flowers, but they reflect a remarkable level of skill for an enterprise that had been in active production for little more than eight years when these coolers were made.

References: Dauterman 1970, pp. 226–27, no. 93a, b, ill.; Jeffrey Munger in Kisluk-Grosheide 2005, pp. 89, 91, fig. 45.

97. Potpourri vase (*pot-pourri gondole*)

Sèvres, 1756–57
Model designed by Jean-Claude Duplessis
(active 1748–74); decoration attributed to
Charles-Nicolas Dodin (active 1754–1803)
Soft-paste porcelain
H. 14⅛ in. (35.9 cm), w. 14½ in. (36.8 cm),
d. 8 in. (20.3 cm)
Gift of Samuel H. Kress Foundation, 1958
(58.75.88a–c)

This vase was made with an elaborate
pierced design in the upper section of
the gondola-shaped body, and there is
an even more complex set of piercings
in the lobed, domed cover, all of which
would have allowed the piece to hold
potpourri. However, the rich ground

color, lavish gilding, and superb painted
decoration suggest that the primary
function of the vase was decorative.
That this potpourri vase probably once
joined two elephant-head vases, now
in the Wallace Collection, London, to
form a garniture on a mantelpiece or

chest of drawers underscores its
essentially decorative nature.

The openwork sections of the
vase, which comprise almost half of
the total design, illustrate the extraordinary skill of the workers at Sèvres.
To cut the openings in the raw clay
and to fire the vase successfully without having those sections warp or
collapse reflect a remarkable technical
mastery. Equally impressive is the
subtle three-dimensional modeling of
the flowers in the openwork panels of
the cover. Every aspect of the production of this vase demonstrates why
Sèvres was regarded as the preeminent porcelain factory in Europe by
the middle of the eighteenth century.
Much of the factory's success was due
to the financial support provided by
Louis XV and to the patronage of the
king and Madame de Pompadour, his
mistress, who owned this vase and
kept it in her apartment at Versailles.

The factory's production remained
at an extremely high level of quality
until the French Revolution, and the
regard in which it was held was noted
by the British traveler Joseph Cradock,
who wrote in June 1784, "Went with
a party by water to Sêve, to examine
the celebrated Porcelain manufactory,
which for brilliancy of colour, and
delicacy of execution, is still believed
to be unrivalled."[1]

1. Cradock 1828, vol. 2, p. 67.

References: Carl Christian Dauterman in
Dauterman, Parker, and Standen 1964,
pp. 199–201, no. 35, figs. 143, 144; Posner
1990, p. 91, fig. 10; Jeffrey Munger in Kisluk-
Grosheide 2005, pp. 89–90, 91, fig. 46.

98. Potpourri vase
(*pot-pourri à vaisseau*)

Sèvres, 1757–58
Model attributed to Jean-Claude Duplessis
(active 1748–74)
Soft-paste porcelain
H. 17½ in. (44.5 cm), w. 15⅛ in. (38.4 cm),
d. 8 in. (20.3 cm)
Gift of Samuel H. Kress Foundation, 1958
(58.75.89a,b)

99. Pair of vases
(*vase à tête d'éléphant*)

Sèvres, ca. 1758
Model designed by Jean-Claude Duplessis
(active 1748–74)
Soft-paste porcelain
H. 15½ in. (39.4 cm), w. 10⅛ in. (25.7 cm),
d. 6 in. (15.2 cm)
Gift of Samuel H. Kress Foundation, 1958
(58.75.90a,b, 91a,b)

Many of the more extraordinary and
unusual vase models made at Sèvres
were created in the late 1750s, and of
these the two types of vases seen here
are among the most novel and ambitious. Such extravagant shapes were
not admired by everyone, however.
Thomas Bentley, the partner of pottery maker Josiah Wedgwood, wrote
in 1776, "'I observed several very
rich vases of the manufacture of Seve,
of the worst and clumsiest forms
imaginable."[1] The majority of these
new vase models found favor at the
French court, however, and contemporary documents indicate that the
elephant-head vases in particular
were avidly purchased by the king,
members of his circle, and prominent
marchands-merciers.

An inventory of 1779 indicates
that the potpourri vase in the form of

Fig. 55. Plaster model for the Sèvres vase
in the form of a ship (*pot-pourri à vaisseau*).
Archives, Manufacture Nationale de Sèvres.

Fig. 56. Plaster model for the pair of Sèvres
vases with two elephant heads (*vase à tête
d'éléphant*). Archives, Manufacture Nationale
de Sèvres.

98 (center), 99 (left; right)

a ship (no. 98) and the two elephant-head vases (no. 99) were part of a decorative grouping of vases that was purchased by Louis-Joseph de Bourbon, prince de Condé (1736–1818), in December 1758. The two other vases that completed the garniture are now in the Musée du Louvre, Paris. The prince de Condé kept the group in his Parisian residence, the Palais de Bourbon. The garniture of five vases cost the prince the impressive sum of 4,320 livres, an amount that exceeded the annual income of a typical professional worker in the eighteenth century.

Madame de Pompadour was an avid buyer of both models of vase, owning at least two of the boat-shaped vases and possessing at least three pairs of elephant-head vases. The cost of these vases and the difficulty of producing them ensured

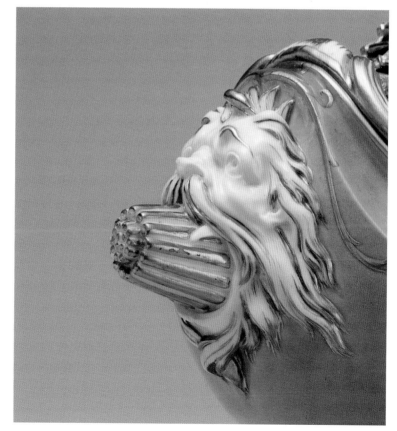

98 (detail)

that relatively few were made. Ten of the boat-shaped vases and twenty-two elephant-head vases are believed to have survived to the present day.

1. Bentley 1776/1977, p. 44.

References for no. 98: Carl Christian Dauterman in Dauterman, Parker, and Standen 1964, pp. 193–95, no. 32, figs. 135, 136; Savill 1988, vol. 1, pp. 155, 192, 196, n. 3a.

References for no. 99: Carl Christian Dauterman in Dauterman, Parker, and Standen 1964, pp. 202–3, no. 36a, b, figs. 145, 146; Savill 1988, vol. 1, pp. 155–56, 161, n. 3e, 197, n. 33.

100. Pair of potpourri vases with candleholders (*pot-pourri à bobêche*)

Sèvres, 1759–60
Model attributed to Jean-Claude Duplessis
(active 1748–74)
Soft-paste porcelain
H. 9⅝ in. (24.4 cm), w. 6⅛ in. (15.6 cm),
d. 3⅝ in. (9.2 cm)
Gift of Samuel H. Kress Foundation, 1958
(58.75.94, 95)

These potpourri vases with candleholders reflect the quest for innovation that characterizes so much of the Sèvres factory's production of the 1760s. The vases could have been used as potpourris (the scent of petals inside could waft through the panels of pierced trelliswork at the top), and the two flanking candle sockets allowed them also to serve as candelabra, yet it seems probable that they were primarily intended for decoration. Both the unusual and complex form and the dual ground colors of

196

Front of the second vase (detail)

Back of the second vase (detail)

pink and green made them completely unlike anything being produced elsewhere on the Continent or in Britain at this time.

As mentioned earlier, the English businessman Thomas Bentley disliked some of the models he saw at the Sèvres factory when he visited there in 1776, and he enlarged on the topic in his journal: "They have an *immense* number of ornamental vases, highly enriched with enamel and burnished gold; and amongst *several hundreds* there may be about *half a dozen* very elegant forms. All the rest are neither antique nor gothic, but barbarous beyond conception."[1] The design of the potpourri vases must have appealed to Louis XV, however, as he purchased four with pink and green grounds in December 1760.

Given the rarity of this model— approximately fifteen surviving examples with a variety of ground colors are known—it is probable that this pair was part of that purchase. The factory sales records indicate that the four potpourri vases acquired by the king were to join another model of vase to form a garniture.

1. Bentley 1776/1977, p. 74.

References: Brunet and Préaud 1978, p. 155, no. 96, ill.; Eriksen and Bellaigue 1987, p. 320, no. 133, ill. p. 321; Jeffrey Munger in Kisluk-Grosheide 2005, pp. 90, 91, fig. 47.

101. Pair of three-light sconces (*bras de cheminée*)

Sèvres, ca. 1760–61
Model attributed to Jean-Claude Duplessis
(active 1748–74)
Soft-paste porcelain; gilt bronze
H. 17⅜ in. (44.1 cm)
Gift of R. Thornton Wilson, in memory of
Florence Ellsworth Wilson, 1954
(54.147.20a–d, 21a–d)

In the 1760s and 1770s in particular, the Sèvres factory consistently introduced products with new forms, new types of decoration, and even new functions. Until that time, sconces of high quality were made either of gilt bronze (see no. 58) or gilt wood. It was a significant technical achievement to produce them in porcelain, and small firing cracks on these objects in areas where the porcelain curves testify to the difficulties involved.

Perhaps the challenges in molding and firing porcelain sconces explain why so few of them were produced. About twenty pairs were made at Sèvres between 1761 and 1768, the period during which these remarkable objects would have been in fashion. Their pronounced scrolling forms incorporating leaves and berries and their sinuous profile epitomize high Rococo design in the decorative arts. They were clearly held in high esteem; Madame de Pompadour owned two pairs, and Louis XV acquired at least ten with a green ground in 1762.

102. Pair of covered vases (*vase en tour*)

Sèvres, ca. 1763
Soft-paste porcelain
H. 22½ in. (57.1 cm), diam. 7¾ in. (19.7 cm)
Gift of R. Thornton Wilson, in memory of
Florence Ellsworth Wilson, 1956
(56.80.1a,b, 2a,b)

Because of the functional nature of services made for dining or for tea, the models of these useful wares changed infrequently at Sèvres. In addition, it was not feasible from an economic standpoint to constantly invent new forms for all of the components of these services. However, for decorative objects such as vases, usually made in pairs or to form a garniture (a set of three or five), the factory was able not only to respond quickly to changing fashions, but also to demonstrate its ability to push the boundaries of ceramic design.

These remarkable vases are in the shape of a fortified tower, with buttresses encircling the top of the body. Small gilt-porcelain cannons extend from underneath the buttresses, the

102 (detail)

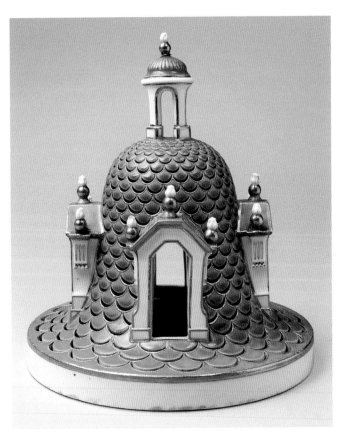

lids are formed as high domes with dormer windows, and a cupola serves as the finial (see detail below). The body is painted with trophies of war, composed of various elements associated with military campaigns (see detail left and page x). The painting is both unusually fine and detailed, suggesting that the vases may have been commissioned for a specific person. However, a precise description in the factory's list of unsold stock in 1770 indicates that they had neither found a buyer nor been given as a gift. Although their early history is unknown, the vases reflect the Sèvres factory's interest in the creation of extraordinary objects that had no precedent in the medium of ceramics.

References: Brunet and Préaud 1978, p. 78, pl. xxx; Jeffrey Weaver in Bennett and Sargentson 2008, pp. 221–24, under no. 87, fig. 91.

103. Punch bowl (*jatte à punch*)

Sèvres, 1771–72
Decoration attributed to Louis-Denis Armand the Elder (active 1746–88)
Soft-paste porcelain
H. 6⁹⁄₁₆ in. (16.7 cm), diam. 13 in. (33 cm)
Gift of Mr. and Mrs. Charles Wrightsman, 1976
(1976.155.162)

The table services produced at Sèvres in the eighteenth century were highly prized and extremely expensive. They were not only purchased by the Crown and members of the aristocracy but also given by the king as diplomatic gifts to foreign courts and visiting dignitaries, and the esteem in which they were held did much to enhance

102 (detail)

103

103 (detail)

103 (detail)

the factory's prestige and fortunes. Because the number of pieces composing a service was very large, the cost was enormous, but this did not deter many courtiers from ordering a dinner or dessert service, or both.

One of the most celebrated services produced at Sèvres was delivered to Louis-René-Édouard, prince de Rohan-Guémenée (1734–1803), on September 7, 1772. All of the pieces were decorated with the rich turquoise ground color known as *bleu céleste* and with birds encircled by an elaborate gilt wreath of oak leaves and acorns. Many of the components of the service bear the initials *LPR* (for Louis, prince de Rohan), executed in two tones of gilding (see detail above). The service cost the substantial sum of 20,772 livres, which was roughly equivalent to twice the annual income of a successful doctor at the time.

This punch bowl is one of twenty-three pieces from the Rohan service now in the Museum's collection. Originally composed of 368 pieces, the service was small in size compared

to other Sèvres services, but the rich use of gilding, the expensive ground color, and the initials in two tones of gold account for its high cost.

Reference: Dauterman 1970, pp. 261–71, no. 109, ill. (see esp. pp. 265–67)

104. Pair of vases (*vase chinois*)

Sèvres, 1791
Decoration by Louis-François L'Écot (active 1763–65, 1772–1802)
Hard-paste porcelain, gilt bronze
H. 14⁵⁄₁₆ in. (36.4 cm), w. 5¼ in. (13.3 cm), d. 4⅝ in. (11.7 cm)
Gift of Mr. and Mrs. Charles Wrightsman, 1971 (1971.206.23, 24)

Fashions changed quickly in France during the eighteenth century, but the taste for decoration in the Chinese style and for black lacquer never waned. This pair of vases, which dates from the last decade of the century, reflects a model known at the Sèvres factory as *vase chinois*, and the handles in the form of the head of a fantastic beast allude to the exoticism then associated with China. The decoration, executed in platinum and two tones of gold, evokes Chinese landscapes in the depiction of craggy rocks, twisting tree branches, and pagodas, and the dress and hairstyles of the figures are clearly intended to suggest Asians. The gold chinoiserie scenes on a black ground are the porcelain equivalent of Japanese black lacquer. The taste for "black lacquer

104 (detail)

porcelain" coincided with the popularity at the French court of furniture mounted with panels of Japanese lacquer (see nos. 52, 53).

It is likely that this pair of vases was owned by Louis XVI. The factory archives record that two *vases chinois* were purchased by the king at the sale of Sèvres porcelain held at Versailles from late December 1791 to mid-January 1792. Their sale price of 1,920 livres is consistent with the lavishness of the decoration seen on this pair.

References: Dauterman 1970, pp. 223–24, no. 91a, b, ill.; Brunet and Préaud 1978, p. 222, no. 294, ill.; Eriksen and Bellaigue 1987, p. 352, no. 157, ill.

105. Cup and saucer (*tasse à l'étrusque et soucoupe*)

Sèvres, 1794
Decoration by Louis-Gabriel Chulot
(active 1755–1800)
Soft-paste porcelain
Cup h. 3³⁄₁₆ in. (8.1 cm); saucer diam. 6⅝ in.
(16.8 cm)
Purchase, Gifts in memory of Henry Chase and
The Charles E. Sampson Memorial Fund, 1990
(1990.101.1, 2)

The lighthearted whimsy of the painted decoration of this cup and saucer is surprising considering the date at which it was executed, for in 1794 the period of repression and mass executions known as the Terror, which followed the French Revolution, was just ending. The decorative scheme is composed of four reserves (panels) of butterflies masquerading as humans. Their gestures and costumes reflect a decidedly playful spirit, despite the dueling depicted in one scene, and several of their poses and the portrayal of one as Harlequin are references to the popular theatrical tradition of the Italian Comedy. Three of the four scenes are copied, with some variations, from a set of six etchings entitled *Essai de papilloneries humaines* by Charles-Germain de Saint-Aubin (1721–1786) that were published shortly after 1756 (see fig. 57).

The painter of the cup and saucer, Louis-Gabriel Chulot, has skillfully captured the spirit of Saint-Aubin's compositions, in which the anthropomorphic butterflies cavort and gesticulate with a sense of levity that is characteristic of much Rococo art. It is surprising that this almost frivolous decorative scheme from the 1750s would have found favor at the very end of the century, just after the French Revolution and at a time when a restrained Neoclassicism predominated. The classically inspired form of the cup reflects the prevailing Neoclassical taste, yet the playful and whimsical nature of the decoration triumphs over the sobriety of form.

References: Clare Le Corbeiller in "Recent Acquisitions" 1990, p. 28, ill.; Le Corbeiller 1994, pls. I, II.

Fig. 57. *Théatre Italien*, from Charles-Germain de Saint-Aubin, *Essai de papilloneries humaines*, ca. 1756. Etching. The Metropolitan Museum of Art, New York, The Elisha Whittelsey Collection, The Elisha Whittelsey Fund and Rogers Fund, 1982 (1982.1101.2).

Silver

JEFFREY MUNGER

Silversmithing flourished in France during the seventeenth and eighteenth centuries, and the silver produced for court and aristocratic circles set the standard for silversmiths elsewhere on the Continent and in Britain. However, French silver of the seventeenth century in particular survives in extremely limited quantities. In 1689 Louis XIV issued a decree that all silver in the kingdom be melted down; the resulting bullion would be used to mint new coinage and replenish the state treasury. In December of that year the prolific letter writer Madame de Sévigné observed that the king had set a good example for his subjects by having his finest silver sent to the Mint.[1] As a consequence of this and later sumptuary edicts, many of the magnificent silver objects produced during his reign were destroyed, including the famous silver furniture produced for Versailles. Our knowledge today of Louis XIV–period silver is based on paintings and prints that show examples and on a relatively few surviving pieces, some of which escaped destruction because they were owned outside of France. The silver that was not destroyed as a result of the king's dictates was often sacrificed to changes in taste, for it was less expensive to have silver melted and then remade in the latest fashion than to commission entirely new pieces.

The very high quality of much eighteenth-century French silver is due in large part to a rigorous system of training required by the guild. An aspiring silversmith customarily had to serve an eight-year apprenticeship followed by three years as a journeyman, at which point he could apply to become a master. In order to be granted this status, the applicant had to pass an examination and submit a work on which he would be judged, which is the origin of the term "masterpiece." The high level of craftsmanship was reinforced by guild regulations regarding the marking of silver. They ensured that the silver standard was strictly maintained, that a maker's mark was struck, and that obligatory taxes were paid.

Changes in dining customs influenced the design of French silver. The late seventeenth century saw the introduction of the *service à la française*, which required that multiple serving dishes be arranged on the table in a symmetrical manner during each course (see figs. 58, 59). Thus, silver moved from decorative displays on sideboards to the table, where its role was primarily functional, although it provided a decorative aspect as well. Diners helped themselves from the platters, dishes, and tureens that were within reach, and a large variety of forms were developed not only to contain the various foods but also to create a pleasing arrangement.

Guild regulations and standards changed with the French Revolution, and new dining customs introduced in the early nineteenth century altered the way in which silver was used at the table. Post-revolutionary French silver rarely displays the quality achieved earlier in the eighteenth century, when superb craftsmanship and lavish patronage allied to produce what are commonly regarded as some of the finest works in silver ever made.

1. Sévigné 1647–96/1927, vol. 7, p. 108.

Fig. 58. Martin van Meytens, *Coronation Banquet of Joseph II in Frankfurt* (detail), 1764. Oil on canvas. Silver Collection, Imperial Apartments, Hofburg, Vienna. On loan from the Kunsthistorisches Museum, Vienna.

Fig. 59. *Table with Fifteen or Sixteen Place Settings*, engraving in Vincent La Chapelle, *Le Cuisinier Moderne* (The Hague, 1742). Schlesinger Library, Radcliffe Institute, Harvard University, Cambridge, Massachusetts.

106. Fork and spoon

Paris, 1683–84
Marked by Louis Nicolle (master in 1666)
Gilt silver
Fork l. 7⅛ in. (18.1 cm); spoon l. 7 in. (17.8 cm)
Bequest of Catherine D. Wentworth, 1948
(48.187.214, 215)

This matching fork and spoon are significant not only as rare survivors of Louis XIV's sumptuary edicts but also as early examples of silver flatware. Although spoons had been used at table since the fifteenth century, forks came into widespread use only in the early part of the seventeenth century, and the concept of a matched fork and spoon, known as a *couvert*, did not appear until the second half of the century. Knives were included in the *couvert* toward the end of the

1600s, shortly after this fork and spoon were made. Gilding and engraved scrolling vegetal motifs decorate other surviving *couverts* of the 1680s.

References: Dennis 1960, no. 261, ill.; Clare Le Corbeiller in Parker et al. 1989, pp. 55, 64, ill.

107. Pair of candlesticks

Paris, 1690–91
Marked by Jacques Demé (master in 1656)
Silver
H. 9¼ in. (23.5 cm), w. 5⅛ in. (13 cm)
Bequest of Catherine D. Wentworth, 1948
(48.187.249, 250)

In both shape and decoration, these candlesticks are early examples of a model that enjoyed great popularity

in France from about 1690 through the 1720s. The octagonal baluster stem and base and the areas of densely patterned ornamentation are characteristic of the majority of candlesticks produced at the end of Louis XIV's reign and in the early years of the minority of Louis XV, called the Régence. The chased decoration of foliate ornament, medallions with profile heads, and bands of strapwork reflect the influence of the court designer Jean Bérain. Bérain's numerous ornament prints provided models for the decoration of silver, ceramics, furniture, and wall paneling, and the so-called Bérainesque style dominated the designs of these media during the years 1680 to 1720.

These candlesticks are marked by the silversmith Jacques Demé and bear the Paris warden's mark for 1690–92. Because silver was not sufficiently durable in its pure state, small amounts of copper were added to provide strength. The copper-to-silver ratio was strictly regulated by the silversmiths' guild, and the presence of the warden's mark indicates that the pieces of silver met the Paris standard of 958.33 parts pure silver per thousand. The French system of marking silver required not only the maker's and warden's marks but also a mark acknowledging the obligation to pay a tax on the piece of silver and another indicating that payment had been made.

References: Dennis 1960, no. 105, ill.; Koeppe 1989, pp. 67–68, fig. 5; Clare Le Corbeiller in Parker et al. 1989, pp. 50–51, 64, ill.; Bimbenet-Privat 2002, vol. 2, pp. 116–17, no. 36, ill.

108. Teapot

Paris, 1699–1700
Marked by "I. C."
Silver; ebony handle
H. 5⅝ in. (14.3 cm), w. with handle 11⅝ in.
(29.5 cm)
Bequest of Catherine D. Wentworth, 1948
(48.187.78)

Tea was still a relatively new beverage in France when this teapot was produced. As the leaves were not imported into France in significant quantities at the time, it was an expensive drink, available only to members of the upper strata of society, and the small size of this teapot reflects tea's high cost. This example appears to be the only surviving Parisian teapot of the late seventeenth century. Tea never gained the popularity of either hot chocolate or coffee in France, and silver teapots do not seem to have been produced in large quantities even in the eighteenth century.

In its design, the teapot corresponds closely to one in a drawing by the silversmith Nicolas-Ambroise Cousinet (active 1696–1715). An inscription indicates that the teapot in Cousinet's drawing was made for Louis, duc d'Aumont (1667–1723), and it is known that the drawing was sent to the Swedish court in 1702. French silversmiths set the artistic standard for court silver throughout Europe, and the Swedes were particularly enamored of French fashions.

References: Dennis 1960, no. 79, ill.; Clare Le Corbeiller in Parker et al. 1989, pp. 54, 64, ill.; Bimbenet-Privat 2002, vol. 2, pp. 258–59, no. 97, ill.

109. Ewer and basin

Paris, 1739–42
Marked by Jean Fauche (ca. 1706–1762)
Silver
Ewer h. 9⁵⁄₁₆ in. (23.7 cm), w. 6½ in. (16.5 cm),
d. 4¾ in. (12.1 cm); basin h. 2⁹⁄₁₆ in. (6.6 cm),
w. 13¹⁵⁄₁₆ in. (35.4 cm), d. 8⁹⁄₁₆ in. (21.7 cm)
Bequest of Catherine D. Wentworth, 1948
(48.187.411, 412)

Before the eighteenth century, custom called for the washing of hands at the table in a grand household. Often one servant held a basin for the diners while another poured water from a ewer. This practice was particularly important before the use of forks became widespread (see entry for no. 106), but by the early eighteenth century, sets of matching forks, knives, and spoons were in common use. Thus, after about 1700 large-scale ewers and basins were produced primarily for display purposes and would have been housed on a sideboard or a tiered buffet. By contrast, smaller ewers and basins such as this example were made for use as part of the toilette, the daily bathing and grooming ritual that took place in the bedroom.

The undulating line of the molded band at the neck of the ewer, the irregularly shaped cartouche beneath the spout, the molded swirling leaves on its cover, and the sinuous lines of

the pierced handle show how the formal, highly organized decorative schemes of the preceding Régence period evolved into a new style in which curvilinear forms and the asymmetrical use of motifs derived from nature predominated. The snail on the handle of the ewer, its shell thumbpiece, and the undulating profile of the basin are other elements that reflect the influence of the new Rococo style, which reached its apex in the middle decades of the eighteenth century.

References: Dennis 1960, no. 135, ill.; *Les Grands Orfèvres* 1965, pp. 134–35, ill.

110. Covered bowl and stand

Strasbourg, ca. 1756
Marked by either Joachim-Frédéric Kirstein I
(master in 1729) or Jean-Frédéric Krug (master
in 1739)
Gilt silver
Bowl h. 4½ in. (11.4 cm), w. 11⅝ in. (29.5 cm);
stand diam. 9⅞ in. (25.1 cm)
The Lesley and Emma Sheafer Collection,
Bequest of Emma A. Sheafer, 1973
(1974.356.679a,b, 680)

Covered bowls such as this, known in France as *écuelles*, were intended for serving hot broth or soup. During the early eighteenth century, broth or bouillon was commonly consumed in the bedroom in the morning during the toilette, the elaborate washing and dressing ritual. The bowl's cover kept the contents warm, and the broth could be sipped from the bowl by using the two handles, while bread rested on the stand. As the eighteenth century progressed, the morning toilette became a less important ritual, and chocolate, coffee, and tea supplanted broth as morning beverages.

This gilt-silver *écuelle* is notable for its Rococo-style handles, composed of overlapping, irregularly shaped cartouches, and for the high quality of the chasing of the decorative band

110 (detail)

Leather case for the covered bowl and stand (original)

encircling the finial on the cover (see detail page 212). This relatively small area is decorated with a waterfowl swimming among reeds, a goat, and sprays of flowers, all intended to provide visual delight to the owner of the *écuelle* when lifting the cover.

Écuelles and stands were also made in porcelain at Sèvres (see no. 95), and though expensive, they were considerably less costly than those produced in silver. The additional step of gilding the silver added further expense, and an *écuelle* such as this one was intended for a very affluent client. Much of the silver produced in Strasbourg in the eighteenth century was gilded, presumably a reflection of local taste.

dynamic movement. The placement of the handle at a right angle to the spout was intended to facilitate pouring, and this feature is commonly found on French coffee and chocolate pots of the middle decades of the eighteenth century. This example was made by François-Thomas Germain, one of the most fashionable and highly regarded silversmiths working in Paris in the second half of the century. It is unusual that Germain signed this piece; the short inscription with his name is located just inside the silver portion of the handle.

Fig. 60. Jean-Étienne Liotard, *Le Déjeuner de Famille*, 1750. Pastel. Private collection.

111. Coffeepot

Paris, 1756–57
Marked by François-Thomas Germain
(1726–1791)
Silver; ebony handle
H. 11⅝ in. (29.5 cm), w. with handle 12 in. (30.5 cm)
Purchase, Joseph Pulitzer Bequest, 1933
(33.165.1)

The design of this coffeepot marks it as one of the most original and striking pieces of eighteenth-century French silver that has come down to us. Its function is signaled by the three-dimensional coffee leaves and berries that form the spout and the base of the handle (see detail right), and the spiral fluting of the body imbues the pot with a sense of

The coffeepot is extremely similar in design to six pots made for King José I as part of a large dinner service produced during a nine-year period commencing in 1756, the year he acceded to the throne of Portugal. The Metropolitan's pot was made three years earlier than the six produced for the Portuguese court, and slight differences in the design of its lid and the absence of the royal Portuguese arms engraved on the base suggest that it was part of another commission. It is likely that this coffeepot was the first example of this design and served as a model for the six destined for the Portuguese court.

References: Dennis 1960, no. 150, ill.; Le Corbeiller 1977a, p. 396, fig. 1; D'Orey 1991, pp. 44, 46.

112. Tureen

Paris, 1757–59
Marked by Edme-Pierre Balzac (ca. 1705–1786)
Silver
H. 10¼ in. (26 cm), w. 15⅜ in. (39.1 cm),
d. 9⅛ in. (23.2 cm)
Bequest of Catherine D. Wentworth, 1948
(48.187.418a–c)

This tureen belongs to a celebrated silver service that has a long and complex history. Its many components were produced over several decades, and despite the very high quality of all the silver in the service there are no stylistic features that tie the assemblage together. The early history of the service remains obscure; however, it has been suggested recently that a

portion may have been purchased by the Saxon court minister Count Heinrich von Brühl (1700–1763), well known for commissioning the so-called Swan porcelain service from the Meissen factory. As the present service was eventually acquired by Louis-Jean-Marie de Bourbon, duc de Penthièvre, and inherited by his grandson Louis-Philippe, duc d'Orléans (1773–1850), who was king of the French from 1830 to 1848, it has become known as the Penthièvre-Orléans service and is regarded as the only French royal silver service that survives.

This tureen and its mate (now in the Musée du Louvre) were made by Edme-Pierre Balzac, one of the

preeminent silversmiths in Paris, who also contributed round tureens, wine coolers, and cruet stands to the service in the years 1757–61. Balzac's tureens are notable for their highly sculptural finials, and it is possible that the stag attacked by hounds atop this one alludes to the type of stew the tureen might contain. The tureen was originally accompanied by a large oval stand.

Reference: Dennis 1960, no. 36, ill.

113. Chocolate pot

Paris, 1765–66
Marked by François-Thomas Germain
(1726–1791)
Silver; wood handle
H. 9¼ in. (23.5 cm), w. with handle 8¾ in.
(22.2 cm)
Bequest of Catherine D. Wentworth, 1948
(48.187.407)

Chocolate was introduced into France in the late seventeenth century, and it quickly became popular as a morning beverage in particular. A number of French prints from this period illustrate fashionable couples drinking chocolate, indicating that this new hot drink had gained immediate acceptance. Hot chocolate needed to be stirred in order to prevent the chocolate from settling at the bottom of the pot. Thus, most French chocolate pots were equipped with a hole in the lid, concealed by a small cover that swiveled, through which a long stick, known as a *moussoir*, could be inserted for stirring (see fig. 61 and detail above).

   This chocolate pot was produced approximately ten years after the cof-

113 (detail)

feepot by the same silversmith illustrated elsewhere in this book (no. 111). It has the same basic shape as the earlier coffeepot but is decorated in the emerging Neoclassical style. Despite the swirling channels on the body, the chocolate pot lacks the sense of movement that is so pronounced in the coffeepot, and the symmetrical

Fig. 61. N. Bonnart, *Couple Drinking Chocolate*, ca. 1690. Engraving. Bibliothèque Nationale de France, Paris, Département des Estampes et de la Photographie.

arrangement of the motifs on the legs and spout reflects the restraining influence of Neoclassicism. Many of the decorative objects produced in France in the 1760s, such as this chocolate pot, are in the so-called Transitional style, in which Rococo stylistic features are combined with newly fashionable Neoclassical motifs.

Reference: Dennis 1960, no. 163, ill.

114. Set of six forks, spoons, and knives in a leather box

Paris, 1767–71
Flatware: marked by Louis-Joseph Lenhendrick (master in 1747, d. 1783)
Gilt silver, silver
Fork l. 7⅝ in. (19.4 cm); knife l. 8⁷⁄₁₆ in. (21.4 cm); spoon l. 7½ in. (19.1 cm)
Box: tooled and gilt leather, silk
H. 2½ in. (6.4 cm), w. 9½ in. (24.1 cm), d. 8¹⁵⁄₁₆ in. (22.8 cm)
Gift of Mr. and Mrs. Charles Wrightsman, 1979 (flatware: 1979.396.4, 5, 11, 13–15, 17, 18, 20, 22–24, 28, 30, 31–34; box: 1979.396.40)

The tooled leather box contains six *couverts*—the French term for two or more matched pieces of flatware—which in this instance each comprise a fork, spoon, and knife. Six identical *couverts* housed in a similar box are also in the Museum's collection. It is not known for whom these thirty-six pieces of flatware were made because the coats of arms that decorated each fork, knife, and spoon have been erased. However, the two boxes are decorated on the lids with the Noailles arms, suggesting that a member of that distinguished aristocratic family owned the cutlery in the eighteenth century.

The designs of the flatware are unusually elaborate and ambitious, especially in the use of openwork in the stems of the fork and spoon, and in the molded and chased decoration of the knife blades. The amount of work required by the complexity of the designs marks these as especially fine pieces of silver cutlery. The two sets date from the years 1767–71, but the designs of the fork, spoon, and knife closely resemble those of a gilt-silver dessert service made in 1744 by the celebrated silversmith Thomas Germain (1673–1748). Germain's designs were then copied twenty years later by his son, François-Thomas Germain, for a gold *couvert* that formed part of the celebrated service made by the latter for the Portuguese court (see entry for no. 111). One of the many silversmiths who assisted Germain with the Portuguese commission was Louis-Joseph Lenhendrick, whose mark appears on the Museum's flatware. As Lenhendrick had also been apprenticed to the elder Germain, he would have been well acquainted with the design of this *couvert*.

Reference: Carl Christian Dauterman in Watson and Dauterman 1970, pp. 264–68, no. 72, ill.

115. Pair of scallop-shell dishes

Paris, 1772–73
Marked by Jacques-Nicolas Roettiers
(1736–1788)
Silver
(.386) h. 1⅞ in. (4.8 cm), w. 4¾ in. (12.1 cm),
d. 5⅛ in. (13 cm); (.387) h. 1⅞ in. (4.8 cm),
w. 5 in. (12.7 cm), d. 5¼ in. (13.3 cm)
Bequest of Catherine D. Wentworth, 1948
(48.187.386, 387)

These dishes in the form of scallop shells were among the twenty-four of this model included in one of the most famous silver services of the eighteenth century, now known as the Orloff service. The Russian empress Catherine the Great ordered the service in 1770, and it was delivered to her at Saint Petersburg in thirteen or fourteen shipments between 1771 and 1775. Intended for sixty people, it comprised a wide variety of pieces, including tureens, plates, dish covers, candlesticks, sauceboats, saltcellars, spice boxes, and serving spoons.

The scallop-shell form is modeled with great precision. A periwinkle and a dog whelk cling to the exterior (see detail below), and the handle is in the form of a piece of seaweed. Curiously, this highly realistic interpretation of an element from nature has no counterpart in the rest of the service, which otherwise displays a rather formal Neoclassicism. Despite this stylistic incongruity, the twenty-four shells are recorded in bills for the service and in an inventory of it taken in Russia. Their intended function on the dining table is not certain, however. It is possible that they were designed to hold sweetmeats, a term that applied to a range of candied fruits and other types of confections. The immensely costly service, which eventually numbered more than 2,500 pieces, appears initially to have been intended for Catherine's own use, but she gave it to her lover, Count Gregory Orloff (1734–1783). Catherine reacquired the service after Orloff's death, but its gradual dispersal began the following year. A portion of the Orloff service was sold by the Soviet government in the late 1920s and early 1930s, whereupon several pieces entered American collections.

References: Dennis 1960, no. 298, ill.; Clare Le Corbeiller in *Versailles et les tables royales en Europe* 1993, pp. 320–21, no. 226, ill.

116. Tureen

Paris, 1775–76
Marked by Jacques-Nicolas Roettiers
(1736–1788)
Silver
H. 12¼ in. (31.1 cm), w. 15½ in. (39.4 cm),
d. 9⅞ in. (25.1 cm)
Gift of Dorothy C. Livingston, in loving memory of Robert R. Livingston, 1986 (1986.320a–c)

for the craftsmanship involved in their making, the amount of silver employed was an indication of both the importance of the object and the wealth of the owner.

Given all the impressive attributes of this tureen, it is surprising that nothing at all is known of its early history. It has been suggested that the tureen, its mate, and other pieces from the original service were acquired at the time of the French Revolution by the American diplomat Gouverneur Morris, who was serving as minister to France. It appears that Morris brought the silver back to America when he returned in 1794 and that he sold at least some of it to Robert R. Livingston (1746–1813), the distinguished first chancellor of New York State. This tureen descended in the Livingston family until 1986, when it was donated to the Metropolitan Museum.

References: W. H. Adams 2003, p. 273, ill. p. 274; Kei Chan in Walker 2004, p. 109, no. 50, ill.

This tureen is very similar to those in the Orloff service (see entry for no. 115), and it is marked by the silversmith responsible for many pieces in that celebrated set, Jacques-Nicolas Roettiers. He was the son of a prominent silversmith, Jacques Roettiers (1707–1784), and he became one of the most accomplished practitioners of the Neoclassical style in silver. Roettiers's skill as a silversmith is evident in this tureen, which employs bold Neoclassical motifs such as rosettes, acanthus leaves, guilloche molding, and volute feet that are all integrated into a harmonious and elegant composition. The detail and crispness of the motifs are notable, and the finial is a masterful three-dimensional essay in the Neoclassical taste.

The quality of the object is evident not only in its design and execution but also in its significant weight. As works in silver were valued in the eighteenth century more for the intrinsic worth of their metal than

Interior of the tureen lid

Gold Boxes

JEFFREY MUNGER

Small gold boxes intended to hold snuff, a form of powdered tobacco, became an important category of the decorative arts in eighteenth-century France. Those who had acquired the habit considered it necessary to carry tobacco on their person, and most snuffboxes could fit into a pocket (see fig. 62). As the British writer Tobias Smollett noted in 1763, "A true-bred Frenchman dips his fingers, imbrowned with snuff, into his plate filled with ragout; between every three mouthfuls he produces his snuff-box, and takes a fresh pinch with the most graceful gesticulations."[1] Snuffboxes and *étuis de pièces* (small containers for precious objects or necessities) were produced in a variety of materials, including porcelain, tortoiseshell, and domestic lacquer, but the ones made of gold are usually the most significant artistically. Gold snuffboxes began to appear in the 1720s and were produced in significant quantities up to the French Revolution. The types of decoration employed for gold boxes evolved over time, reflecting changes in fashion and the development of new techniques. The boxes of the 1720s and 1730s were usually made entirely of gold, although precious stones were sometimes used to embellish the most costly examples. Beginning in the 1740s, other materials, such as lacquer, mother-of-pearl, or hardstones, were often incorporated into a framework of gold. Boxes decorated in this manner are described in French as being mounted *à cage*. Enamel decoration became popular in the second half of the 1740s. The enamel could be applied directly on the surface of the box (in a technique known as *en plein*) or over areas that had been lightly carved away (*basse taille*). In the following decade, it was discovered that the use of different colors of gold would provide additional richness to a box's decoration. In order to achieve different tonalities, gold was alloyed with small amounts of other metals to

Fig. 62. Maurice Quentin de La Tour, *Portrait of Louis Duval de l'Epinoy*, 1745. Pastel, 47⅛ × 36⅝ in. (119.5 × 92.8 cm). Museu Calouste Gulbenkian, Lisbon (inv. 2380).

create hues of red, green, blue, and white. The 1760s saw the increasing popularity of boxes with miniatures painted on vellum mounted *à cage*. Machine engraving—a process that is known as engine turning—was used frequently in the 1770s and 1780s to produce decorative patterns on metal. On boxes it was often employed in combination with a translucent colored-enamel ground that allowed the pattern beneath to be clearly visible.

This wide variety of decorative techniques allowed the affluent snuff-taker a plenitude of boxes from which to choose, and it was considered desirable to own many different types. The French writer Louis-Sébastien Mercier observed in 1781, perhaps with exaggeration, "There are boxes for each season. The one for winter is heavy; that for summer light. There are those who carry this refinement to the extent of changing boxes every day: it is by this distinctive touch that one may recognize the man of taste. He who has three hundred boxes and as many rings may properly dispense with a library, a natural history collection, and paintings."[2]

The production of gold boxes reached its zenith in the years 1760–80. Thereafter, changing customs, declining fortunes, and the French Revolution impacted gold-box production at the end of the eighteenth century. The boxes that were made in the preceding decades, however, are among the finest examples of French decorative arts in the taste of the ancien régime.

1. Smollett 1766/1969, p. 45.
2. Mercier 1782–83, vol. 2, p. 220.

117. Snuffbox

Paris, 1734–35
Marked by Daniel Gouers (master in 1717)
Gold, diamonds
H. 1 in. (2.5 cm), w. 3¼ in. (8.3 cm), d. 2⅜ in. (6 cm)
Bequest of Catherine D. Wentworth, 1948 (48.187.419)

The use of snuff did not become fashionable in France until after the death in 1715 of Louis XIV, who was known to disapprove of the habit. By the time this gold box was produced, the taking of snuff was an important and elaborate social ritual. Not only were there rules of etiquette for it but the boxes that contained the powdered tobacco became highly desirable and visible accessories, serving as statements about both one's taste and one's financial status. While visiting Paris from England with her great friend Samuel Johnson, Hester Thrale wrote, "We went nowhere to day but to the Great Toy Shop called the Petit Dunkerque; I bought a Trinket or two, & longed for a Snuffbox of exquisite beauty."[1] Boxes were produced at all levels of artistic skill and expense. Only the very rich could afford gold boxes, and gold boxes set with diamonds, such as this one, were the most expensive of all.

Boxes of significant cost often served as discreet forms of payment, as the recipient had the option of returning the box to the jeweler who had sold it and exchanging it for cash. Gold boxes were commonly given by the French monarch to reward service to his court, and the value of the box depended on the status of the person receiving it and the degree of service supplied. Foreign ambassadors were frequent recipients of expensive gold boxes from the king.

This box is a particularly elaborate example; the chased decoration is of very high quality, and inset diamonds have been liberally employed on the lid and front. It bears the mark of Daniel Gouers (also known as Govaers), one of the preeminent goldsmiths of the early eighteenth century, who inscribed "Gouers à Paris" on the bezel. The box is an early example of the Rococo style, seen here in the prominent use of abstract scrolling motifs, the asymmetry of the central decoration on the lid, and the undulating profile of the box's shape.

1. Journal entry for October 26, 1775, in Thrale 1775/1932, p. 143.

Reference: Snowman 1966, pl. 149.

118. Snuffbox

Paris, 1736–37
Marked by Jean Ducrollay (b. 1709; master in 1734)
Gold
H. 1⁹⁄₁₆ in. (4 cm), w. 3⁵⁄₁₆ in. (8.4 cm), d. 2¹¹⁄₁₆ in. (6.8 cm)
Gift of Mr. and Mrs. Charles Wrightsman, 1976 (1976.155.7)

The basic design of snuffboxes was to a certain extent determined by their function. As the ritual of taking snuff required holding the box in one hand while taking a pinch of the powdered tobacco with the other, a snuffbox had to fit comfortably in the palm of one's hand. The use of a hinged lid on the box minimized any spillage, and the lid had to fit very snugly in order to keep the snuff dry. In addition, the box had to open to a precise angle that would permit easy access to the contents while allowing it to remain stable with the lid raised. The French gold-box makers became extremely skilled in the techniques of construction, as evidenced here, for example, in the visual absence of solder and the beautifully engineered hinges that were standard on most boxes of the eighteenth century.

Jean Ducrollay was one of the finest of the Parisian goldsmiths, and this is an early example of his work. Like the snuffbox in gold and diamonds made a few years earlier (no. 117), its decoration reflects the nascent Rococo style, which favored a prominent use of scrolls and S-curves and asymmetrical compositions.

Despite the widespread popularity of snuff and the beauty of many of the boxes created to hold it, snuff taking had its detractors, including the sister-in-law of Louis XIV, Élisabeth-Charlotte, duchesse d'Orléans, who wrote to her half-sister Luise von Degenfeld on August 5, 1713: "Tobacco is horrible stuff. I sincerely hope that you don't take it. It makes me furious to see the women here with their noses as dirty as if they had plunged them into filth. They put their fingers into the snuff boxes of every man they meet. I confess that makes me thoroughly disgusted."[1]

1. Orléans 1661–1722/1924–25, vol. 2, p. 67.

119. Box

London, 1741
Marked by "P. R."; chased by George Michael
Moser (1706–1783)
Gold
H. 1⁹⁄₁₆ in. (4 cm), w. 4⁹⁄₁₆ in. (11.6 cm), d. 3½ in.
(8.9 cm)
Gift of Mr. and Mrs. Charles Wrightsman, 1976
(1976.155.23)

Although this box is one of the finest surviving examples of eighteenth-century English goldsmiths' work, little is known about its manufacture and history, or even its intended function. The comparatively large size of the box suggests that it was not meant to contain snuff but rather may have served as a presentation box, intended to reward a specific feat or service. The box is marked with the initials "P. R.," which have been interpreted as the mark of a silversmith named Peter Russell, but this identification is far from conclusive. The only secure information is provided by the signature on the lid of George Michael Moser, followed by the date 1741. Moser was a chaser, the term for those who worked the surface of metal with hammers and punches in order to create low-relief decoration.

Born in Switzerland, Moser appears to have learned the skills of chasing and gilding from his father, and he moved to England in 1726 in search of better opportunities in his trade. By the late 1730s he was established as an independent gold chaser in London, and early in the following decade he was already recognized for his outstanding abilities. At Moser's death, the court painter Sir Joshua Reynolds (1723–1792) praised his chasing skills, "in which art he has always been considered as holding the first rank."[1]

Moser's abilities are readily apparent in the complex and beautifully executed compositions that decorate the top and bottom of this box. The cover is chased with a scene depicting the Roman hero Gaius Mucius Scaevola before the Etruscan king Lars Porsena. The underside of the box depicts the twin founders of Rome, Romulus and Remus, suckled by a wolf in front of a river god personifying the Tiber. In the clarity of forms and precision of detail, and especially in the fluid transition from low to high relief, Moser's work reflects chasing at its highest level of skill.

1. *Public Advertiser*, January 30, 1783, quoted in Edgcumbe 2000, p. 85.

Reference: Edgcumbe 2000, pp. 99–102, figs. 81a–c.

Bottom of the box

Top of the box

120. Box

Paris, 1748–49
Marked by Pierre-François Delafons (master in 1732)
Gold
H. 1¾ in. (4.4 cm), w. 3⅛ in. (7.9 cm), d. 2¼ in. (5.7 cm)
Miniatures: attributed to Louis-Nicolas van Blarenberghe (1716–1794), 1767
Gouache on vellum
Gift of Mr. and Mrs. Charles Wrightsman, 1976 (1976.155.22)

The miniatures that decorate this box lend it unusual importance and interest. The six scenes, which are painted in gouache on vellum, depict views of the Château de Chanteloup and of the gardens that surrounded it. The miniature on the lid, which provides the primary view of the château, is signed "Van Blarenberghe 1767." Three members of the Van Blarenberghe family painted miniatures, but these views of Chanteloup are attributed to Louis-Nicolas, considered the most talented of the three. His skills as a miniaturist were exceptional, and the small body of his work that survives provides an extraordinary record of various aspects of French life in the second half of the eighteenth century.

Chanteloup was owned by Étienne-François de Choiseul-Stainville, duc de Choiseul (1719–1785). As a principal governmental minister to Louis XV, and supported by the king's mistress, Madame de Pompadour, Choiseul was one of the most powerful men in France until his political downfall in 1770. He retreated to Chanteloup and never returned to public life.

In addition to commissioning the views of Chanteloup from Van Blarenberghe, Choiseul asked the

Bottom of the box

artist to paint miniatures of the interiors of his Parisian house, the Hôtel de Choiseul, to be incorporated into a snuffbox similar to the Chanteloup box (private collection). The two Choiseul boxes are remarkable documents of the residences of one of the most important and colorful figures of the ancien régime.

The gold frame into which the miniatures have been inserted bear the Paris warden's mark for 1748–49. Boxes constructed with framework in this manner allowed for miniatures to be replaced as demands of fashion dictated.

References: Le Corbeiller 1966, p. 27 and fig. 52; Watson 1966a, pp. 156–58, pls. 264–66; Francis J. B. Watson in Watson and Dauterman 1970, pp. 133–39, no. 8, ill.; Le Corbeiller 1977b, no. 15, ill.; Hall 2009, figs. 1, 2.

121. Snuffbox

Paris, 1753–54
Marked by Noël Hardivillers (active 1729–79)
Gold, enamel
H. 1½ in. (3.8 cm), w. 3 1⁄16 in. (7.8 cm), d. 2 5⁄16 in. (5.9 cm)
Gift of Mr. and Mrs. Charles Wrightsman, 1976
(1976.155.5)

This box is a brilliant example of enamel decoration on gold. The oval scenes on the lid, sides, and base are created by enameling directly on the flat gold surface, the process known as *en plein*. In contrast, much of the translucent green enamel that surrounds the scenes is applied to small

Bottom of the box

Fig. 63. Duflos after François Boucher, *La Poésie Pastorale*, after 1741. Etching. The Metropolitan Museum of Art, New York, Harris Brisbane Dick Fund, 1953 (53.600.1025)

areas of the gold that have been engraved or carved away, the technique referred to as *basse taille*. The quality of both types of enameling is extremely high and is likely the work of a specialist. Frequently the goldsmith who produced a box turned

to another artisan when a highly specialized type of decoration, such as enameling or the incorporation of lacquer, was required.

The scenes decorating the lid and the underside of this box are based on works by the French painter François

Boucher (1703–1770). The enameler has copied Boucher's painting *Pensent-Ils au Raisin?* (Nationalmuseum, Stockholm) for the scene on the lid, and *La Poésie Pastorale* (known only through etchings; see fig. 63) for the one on the underside. Prints after these and other paintings by Boucher were widely disseminated and served repeatedly as compositional models for enamelers and porcelain painters. Scenes after Boucher were among the most popular types of decoration on French decorative arts of all media in the mid-eighteenth century.

References: Francis J. B. Watson in Watson and Dauterman 1970, pp. 140–43, no. 9, ill.; Le Corbeiller 1977b, no. 11, ill.

122

122. Snuffbox

Paris, 1754–55
Marked by Jean Ducrollay (b. 1709; master in 1734)
Gold, lacquer, enamel, and tortoiseshell inlaid with gold
H. 1⁹⁄₁₆ in. (4 cm), w. 3⅛ in. (7.9 cm), d. 2¼ in. (5.7 cm)
Gift of Mr. and Mrs. Charles Wrightsman, 1976 (1976.155.16)

The shaped black panels that decorate the top, bottom, and sides of this box were intended to imitate Japanese lacquer, which was very much in fashion in France throughout the eighteenth century. The six panels are in fact made of tortoiseshell decorated in a technique known as *piqué*, in which extremely thin gold and silver wire is inlaid in the shell. The resulting compositions provide a close approximation of black-and-gold Japanese lacquer. These panels with *piqué* decoration are set into rectangular panels made of imitation red lacquer.

Because of the high cost of importing Japanese lacquer—and the length of time it took the lacquer to reach France—there was considerable impetus to develop a French alternative to Asian lacquers. In 1730 a patent was given to Guillaume Martin (d. 1749). Martin, his brothers, and eventually other members of his family were so successful in producing a French version of Asian lacquer that the term *vernis Martin* became the common designation for all lacquer produced in France in the middle decades of the eighteenth century. Furniture decorated with *vernis Martin* was particularly popular during this period.

The *piqué* and imitation red lacquer panels of this box are set in a gold frame that has been enameled and chased with an overall lozenge pattern. This practice of setting panels of different materials into a gold frame was known as mounting *à cage*. The interior of the box bears the mark of Jean Ducrollay, one of the most prominent Parisian goldsmiths working in the middle decades of the century. One of his specialties was the production of gold boxes with panels of lacquer, both Japanese and French.

References: Snowman 1966, pl. 297; Francis J. B. Watson in Watson and Dauterman 1970, pp. 146–48, no. 11, ill.; Le Corbeiller 1977b, no. 16, ill.

123. Snuffbox

Paris, 1759–62
Marked by Jean George (active 1752–65);
miniatures by Mademoiselle Duplessis
Gold, enamel, and diamonds
H. 1¾ in. (4.4 cm), w. 3⅜ in. (8.6 cm), d. 2⅝ in.
(6.7 cm)
Gift of J. Pierpont Morgan, 1917 (17.190.1125)

This box in the emerging Neoclassical style is distinguished by the quality of both the goldsmith's work and
the enameled decoration. The latter
includes ovals painted in brown
monochrome with putti who frolic
beneath garlands of polychrome flowers across the top of each oval. They
are framed with molded gold borders
and set against rectangular panels
embellished with a scale pattern in
low relief. A garland of flowers encir-
cles the rim of the lid, and pendant
garlands separate the panels containing the ovals. Four colors of gold
have been employed for the various
motifs, adding a subtle yet noticeable
sense of contrast to the different components of the metalwork design. The
cover, set with diamonds encircling
the enameled scene, has a diamond
thumbpiece in the form of a bowknot
with sprays of flowers.

The enamel decoration on the lid
was signed by Mademoiselle Duplessis,
whose name is first recorded in
1753–54, and whose signature appears
on another enameled snuffbox in the
Metropolitan Museum (1976.155.8).

The box itself is signed "George à
Paris" and bears the mark of Jean
George, a highly successful maker of
gold boxes in Paris. A sale of
George's possessions after his death
in 1765 included a "quantity of new
jewelry in the latest taste from the
workshop of Monsieur George, such
as snuffboxes, *étuis*, scent bottles,
patch boxes, candy boxes, shuttles,
étuis de pièces, men's and women's
watches, chains, seals, in gold as well
as in gold and enamel."[1]

1. Quoted in Cocks and Truman 1984, p. 206.

References: Le Corbeiller 1966, fig. 110;
Snowman 1966, pl. 318.

124. Snuffbox

Paris, 1764–65
Possibly made by Pierre-François-Mathis de
Beaulieu (active as master 1768–92)
Gold, enamel
H. 1 ¾ in. (4.4 cm), w. 3 ⅛ in. (7.9 cm), d. 2 ⅜ in.
(6 cm)
Gift of J. Pierpont Morgan, 1917 (17.190.1158)

An oval portrait of Catherine the Great of Russia on the cover of this box is the most prominent feature of its decoration. Catherine ruled Russia as empress from 1762 until her death in 1796, and the small enamel portrait depicts her early in her reign. The underside of the box is decorated with an image of the empress crowned by fame, while the small enamel medallions on the sides depict the four cardinal virtues: fortitude, justice, prudence, and temperance. The decoration thus serves to extol the virtues and qualities of the new empress, who came to power by deposing her husband, Peter III.

The chased motifs are in the full-blown Neoclassical style, and four colors of gold have been employed to enhance their richness. Gold could be colored by adding small amounts of other metals: copper gives gold a warm pinkish hue, and silver creates a slightly greenish tone. Acting as a visual foil to the various colors of gold is the translucent blue enamel, through which the decorative pattern of the gold beneath is visible.

Richly decorated boxes with a portrait of a reigning monarch were frequently given as diplomatic gifts or to reward a special service or favor to the court. These gifts had the dual advantage of conveying great prestige upon the recipient while also being of significant monetary value. It was common practice for monarchs to present gold boxes bearing a portrait of themselves to visiting ambassadors or ministers; the Duke of Manchester, acting as British envoy, received a box from Louis XVI valued at slightly more than 31,000 livres, at a time when a successful doctor in France

might earn 10,000 livres annually.

This box is attributed to the goldsmith Pierre-François-Mathis de Beaulieu, although it bears the mark of Jean George as well as the inscription "George à Paris." The box's design is very similar to that of a slightly later example marked by Beaulieu, who served as an apprentice to George. As Beaulieu did not become a master until 1768, he would have had to use George's mark when this box was made, in 1764–65.

Reference: Le Corbeiller 1966, fig. 145.

Biographical Notes

DANIËLLE KISLUK-GROSHEIDE

Written observations and conversational comments by the persons listed and briefly described below, all of whom are quoted in this book, illuminate our understanding of life in France during the ancien régime, the Revolutionary period, and the early nineteenth century. Each biography is followed by an abbreviated reference to a book or article by or about the subject. Full citations may be found in the bibliography, which begins on page 237. Cross-referenced names, which are themselves entries in these biographical notes, are set in SMALL CAPITAL LETTERS.

Adams, John (1735–1826). Second president of the United States (1797–1801). In 1778 and 1779 he spent time in France as a diplomat, and his letters written home to his wife, Abigail, during that period contain interesting comments about France and the French.
[J. Adams and A. Adams 1774–83/1970]

Argenson, René-Louis de Voyer de Paulmy, marquis d' (1694–1757). French statesman who served his country as minister of foreign affairs from 1744 to 1747. He was a friend of Voltaire and the author of a journal documenting the political and literary life in France during the reign of Louis XV.
[Argenson 1857–58]

Bentley, Thomas (1731–1780). Successful English merchant who became the business partner of Josiah Wedgwood, the well-known manufacturer of pottery, in 1769. He traveled to France on business in 1776, during which time he kept a journal.
[Bentley 1776/1977]

Berry, Mary (1763–1852). English author of several comedies, and the neighbor, friend, and correspondent of HORACE WALPOLE. Before and after the French Revolution she made several trips to France, which she documented in her journals.
[Berry 1783–1852/1866]

Blondel, Jacques-François (1705–1774). Member of a family of French architects. He authored several treatises on architecture and also wrote articles on the same subject for the encyclopedia edited by DENIS DIDEROT. He was a member of the Académie d'Architecture in Paris and became a professor there in 1762. Blondel rebuilt and beautified the city center of Metz and also worked in Strasbourg.
[Blondel 1771–77]

Boigne, Louise-Éléonore-Charlotte-Adélaïde d'Osmond, comtesse de (1781–1866). As the daughter of a lady-in-waiting to Madame Adélaïde, she was born at Versailles and raised at the Château de Bellevue. In 1792 she emigrated with Madame Adélaïde

and another aunt of Louis XVI, Madame Victoire, to Naples. She presided over a popular salon in nineteenth-century Paris and was the author of two novels. Her memoirs are a source of information about the French court during her lifetime, especially during the reign of Louis-Philippe.
[Boigne 1781–1830/1907–8]

Brice, Germain (1652–1727). French historian about whose life little is known. Brice was the author of a popular guide to Paris, which describes in detail the city's public and religious buildings. First published in 1684 as *Description nouvelle de ce qu'il y a de remarquable dans la ville de Paris*, the guide appeared in eight editions, the last one published in 1752.
[Brice 1687]

Campan, Jeanne-Louise-Henriette, née Henriette Genet or Genest (1752–1822). French author and educator. As an intelligent and well-educated fifteen-year-old, she was appointed reader to the daughters of Louis XV. Later she served for many years as lady-in-waiting to Marie-Antoinette. Financially ruined during the Revolution, Madame Campan established a school for girls at Saint-Germain in 1794 (one of the pupils was Hortense de Beauharnais, the stepdaughter of Napoléon). Her memoirs of the court of Louis XVI and Marie-Antoinette were posthumously published in 1823.
[Campan 1823]

Chambers, Sir William (1723–1796). Architect of Scottish descent and the author of several influential architectural treatises. Born in Sweden, he traveled twice to Canton (Guangzhou) in the service of the Swedish East India Company, and there he made drawings that were later used for his *Designs for Chinese Buildings* (1757). Chambers studied in Paris and Rome before he was appointed tutor to the Prince of Wales. He became one of the most important and successful architects in late eighteenth-century England.
[Chambers 1759]

Clérisseau, Charles-Louis (1721–1820). French painter and architectural draftsman. He studied and worked in Rome until 1767, serving as a mentor to artists and young gentlemen on the grand tour, such as WILLIAM CHAMBERS and Robert Adam. Clérisseau's architectural views and drawings of both real Roman ruins and imaginary ones became widely known. Catherine the Great, who was interested in Classical Revival architecture and admired his oeuvre, acquired eighteen portfolios of his work and invited him to come to Russia. None of the architectural projects Clérisseau designed for the empress were realized, however.
[Hautecoeur 1912]

Cole, The Reverend William (1714–1782). English antiquary and historian of Cambridgeshire who served as rector of Bletchley, Buckinghamshire, from 1753 to 1767. He was a diarist, friend, and correspondent of HORACE WALPOLE, whom he met while at school at Eton and visited in Paris in 1765. Cole kept a diary of his journey.
[Cole 1765/1931]

Cradock, Joseph (1742–1826). English author, playwright, and amateur actor, and a friend of the well-known actor and theatrical producer David Garrick. He traveled through France and the Netherlands from 1783 until 1786.
[Cradock 1828]

David d'Angers, Pierre-Jean (1788–1856). French sculptor who began his career in Paris as a pupil of Philippe-Laurent Roland. In 1811 he won the Prix de Rome and studied in Italy for a number of years. David d'Angers is known for his numerous busts and portrait medallions depicting the era's illustrious writers, artists, and politicians.
[Jouin 1878]

Deffand, Marie-Anne de Vichy-Chamrond, marquise du (1697–1780). French aristocrat known for her intelligence and wit, whose Paris salon was visited not only by aristocrats but also by scientists, writers, and philosophers. Later in life she became a close friend of HORACE WALPOLE, twenty years her junior, and she corresponded with him for many years.
[Walpole 1937–83, vols. 3–8 (1939)]

De Piles, Roger (1635–1709). French painter, art critic, and art theorist who also served as a diplomat. He wrote a treatise on color and another on the principles of painting, and in 1681 he published a life of Peter Paul Rubens.
[De Piles 1743]

Dézallier d'Argenville, Antoine-Nicolas (1723–1796). Son of the naturalist and garden theorist Antoine-Joseph Dézallier d'Argenville. Like his father, he wrote on art and gardening. He is best known for his popular guide to the major monuments of Paris, which was first published in 1749 and appeared in five later editions.
[Dézallier d'Argenville 1757]

Diderot, Denis (1713–1784). French philosopher and man of letters. With Jean Le Rond d'Alembert he contributed to and coedited *L'Encyclopédie*, which, because of some of its radical ideas, was at the time of publication viewed with disfavor by the church and by some members of the French establishment. The comprehensive dictionary of the sciences, arts, and crafts appeared in multiple volumes between 1751 and 1772.
[Diderot 1751–72]

Du Coudray, Alexandre-Jacques (1744–1790). About the personal life of this French chevalier and, for a time, musketeer in the service of the king, little is known. He was a historian, author, and theater

critic, and he chronicled the visit of Emperor Joseph II to Paris in 1777.
[Du Coudray 1778]

Dufort de Cheverny, Jean-Nicolas, comte (1731–1802). From 1752 until 1764 this French nobleman held the post of usher for the foreign ambassadors arriving at the court of Louis XV. Later he served as a commandant in the national guard. Imprisoned during the Revolution, he began his memoirs in 1794 and completed them after his release. Written from memory and published after his death, those reminiscences are anecdotal and often amusing.
[Dufort de Cheverny 1794–95/1990]

Duvaux, Lazare (ca. 1703–1758). Parisian dealer in luxury goods, or *marchand bijoutier ordinaire du roi*. Duvaux's daybook for 1748–58 not only reveals the names of his clients (who included Madame de Pompadour, a frequent customer) but also sheds light on the different aspects of his business.
[Duvaux 1748–58/1965]

Eastlake, Lady Elizabeth, née Rigby (1809–1893). English art historian, art critic, and prolific writer. She married Sir Charles Eastlake, director of the National Gallery, London, with whom she led an active social life, traveled, and also collaborated.
[Eastlake 1895]

Feodorovna, Maria (1759–1828). She was Sophie Dorothea of Württemberg before her marriage in 1776 to Grand Duke Paul of Russia. In 1781–82 the couple made a tour of Europe and they visited Paris under the pseudonyms of comte and comtesse du Nord. After their return to Russia they spent time at their summer palace, Pavlovsk, which was built for them by the architect Charles Cameron. Maria Feodorovna wrote a detailed account of the palace and its contents in 1795.
[Feodorovna 1795/1903]

Gibbon, Edward (1737–1794). English historian, author, and a member of Parliament. He is best known for his work *The History of the Decline and Fall of the Roman Empire*, which was published in six volumes between 1776 and 1788. Gibbon set out on a grand tour of continental Europe in 1763, visiting France as well as Italy.
[Gibbon 1788–93/1966]

Hackert, Jakob Philipp (1737–1807). German painter who specialized in gouache landscapes. In 1768 he went to Italy, where he worked for the British ambassador Sir William Hamilton in Naples and also at the court of King Ferdinand IV at Caserta.
[Nordhoff and Reimer 1994]

Johnson, Samuel (1709–1784). One of the most important English authors of the eighteenth century, known for his plays, satires, poetry, biographies, the *Dictionary of the English Language*, and an annotated edition of the works of Shakespeare. He kept a diary during his trip to France in 1775, where he traveled in the company of

his friend HESTER THRALE. Johnson's life was the subject of a famous biography by James Boswell.
[S. Johnson 1775/1932]

Le Camus de Mézières, Nicolas (1721–1783). This French architect built the Halle au Blé in Paris (1763–67). As a theorist, he is best known for his book *Le Génie de l'architecture; ou, L'Analogie de cet art avec nos sensations* (1780), in which he explores the idea that architecture should be pleasing and that the senses can be stimulated by a successful design.
[Le Camus de Mézières 1780/1992]

Lister, Martin (ca. 1638–1712). An English naturalist and physician who wrote numerous articles on natural history and medicine and also several works on shells. His detailed diary of a trip to Paris in 1698 turned out to be a very popular work and was even translated into French.
[Lister 1699]

Luynes, Charles-Philippe d'Albert, duc de (1695–1758). French peer and colonel of a horse regiment. His second wife, Marie Brulart, served as lady-in-waiting to Queen Marie Leszczyńska. Posthumously published, his memoirs document life at the court of Louis XV.
[Luynes 1735–58/1860–65]

***Mémoires secrets pour servir à l'histoire de la République des Lettres en France depuis MDCCLXII jusqu'à nos jours*, Contributors to**. The anonymous chronicle called *Mémoires secrets*, which was probably disseminated in manuscript form as a newspaper, offered detailed descriptions of various political and cultural events that occurred between 1762 and 1787. It has been attributed to Louis Petit de Bachaumont (1690–1771), but since many of the events described took place after his death, it is more probably the work of multiple authors. When the *Mémoires secrets* were published as a set (London, 1783–89), they filled eighteen volumes.
[Popkin and Fort 1998]

Mercier, Louis-Sébastien (1740–1814). French dramatist and prolific author of novels and pamphlets. He is best known for his *Tableau de Paris*, which appeared in twelve volumes between 1781 and 1788. In this work, he chronicled with keen observation daily life in the French capital.
[Mercier 1781–88/1999 and Mercier 1782–83]

Mercy-Argenteau, Florimond-Claude, comte de (1727–1794). An Austrian diplomat who served as minister to Paris from 1766 until 1792. He was a powerful figure at the court of Louis XVI. During his years in France he corresponded extensively with Empress Maria Theresa, the mother of Marie-Antoinette.
[Mercy-Argenteau 1770–80/1874 and Smythe 1770–80/1902]

Morris, Gouverneur (1752–1816). American statesman and author of large sections of the United States Constitution who served as minister plenipotentiary to France from 1792 to 1794. During his years in France he kept a diary that captured life in Paris at the time of the Revolution.
[Morris 1789–93/1939]

Northumberland, Elizabeth Seymour Percy, Duchess of (1716–1776). English aristocrat who served as lady-of-the-bedchamber to Queen Charlotte from 1761 until 1770. In May of that year, she traveled to France to attend the wedding of the dauphin (the future Louis XVI) to Marie-Antoinette, an event the duchess recorded in her diary.
[Northumberland 1752–74/1926]

Oberkirch, Henriette Louise de Waldner de Freundstein, baronne d' (1754–1803). Childhood friend of Grand Duchess MARIA FEODOROVNA, whom she accompanied on the latter's 1782 visit to the French court.
[Oberkirch 1789/1970]

Orléans, Élisabeth-Charlotte, Princess Palatine and duchesse d' (1652–1722). Second wife of Philippe, duc d'Orléans, the younger brother of Louis XIV. She was the mother of Philippe II d'Orléans (1674–1723), who served as regent during the minority of Louis XV. Her many, often candid, letters are a wonderful source of information about the court of Louis XIV and the personalities of his courtiers.
[Orléans 1661–1722/1924–25 and Orléans 1672–1722/1970]

Peckham, Harry (1740–1787). English lawyer, king's counsel, and recorder for Chichester. He was an avid sportsman who played cricket and helped to draw up the early laws of that sport. He toured the Low Countries and France in 1769, and during his travels he wrote a series of witty and perceptive letters, first published in book form in 1772.
[Peckham 1788]

Raynal, Guillaume-Thomas-François, abbé (1713–1796). French Jesuit and thinker who abandoned his ecclesiastical career in favor of a literary one and became a celebrated historian in his lifetime. He edited the periodical *Mercure de France* and wrote several historical works. The most important and popular of the latter was the multivolume *Histoire . . . des Européens dans les deux Indes* (1770), in which he denounced European cruelty to colonial peoples. It infuriated the government, especially as the radical tone of the work increased in subsequent editions, and Raynal was forced into exile for a number of years.
[J. Chanut, "Raynal (Guillaume-Thomas-François)," in *Nouvelle Biographie générale* 1852–66/1963–69, vols. 41–42 (1968), cols. 758–65]

Roubo, André-Jacob (1739–1791). French cabinetmaker and author of an informative manual on woodworking and the making of furniture and related crafts.
[Roubo 1769–75]

Sévigné, Marie de Rabutin-Chantal, marquise de (1626–1696). French aristocrat known for her spirited and charming letters, many of which were addressed to her daughter Françoise, who moved to distant Provence when her husband, the comte de Grignan, became governor there.
[Sévigné 1647–96/1927]

Seymour-Conway, Francis (1718–1794). British courtier and statesman. He was created Viscount Beauchamp and Earl of Hertford in 1750 and a year before his death was elevated to the rank of Marquess. He held a series of posts, including that of lord-of-the-bedchamber, under George II and George III and served as a member of the Privy Council. In 1763 he was appointed ambassador to France, a position he occupied until 1765. He was a cousin of HORACE WALPOLE, with whom he corresponded.
[Walpole 1937–83, vols. 37–39 (1974)]

Smollett, Tobias George (1721–1771). Scottish surgeon with literary ambitions who abandoned medicine to pursue a career in writing. He produced successful picaresque novels and poetry, as well as *A Complete History of England* in several volumes. A sojourn in France and Italy during 1763–65 inspired him to write a lively and observant but often prejudiced travel book in 1766.
[Smollett 1766/1969]

Swinburne, Henry (1743–1803). English traveler and travel author. He made a number of trips to continental Europe, which he documented in various accounts and sometimes illustrated with his own sketches.
[Swinburne 1774–1803/1900]

Thicknesse, Philip (1719–1792). English army captain. A somewhat enigmatic figure, he capitalized on his journeys to the Continent by publishing several travel books.
[Thicknesse 1768]

Thrale, Hester Lynch Salusbury (1741–1821). English author and diarist, acquainted with a number of important contemporary literary figures, such as James Boswell, Fanny Burney, and SAMUEL JOHNSON. She accompanied the latter on his trip to France in 1775. Following the death of her first husband, Henry Thrale, she married an Italian music teacher, Gabriel Mario Piozzi, in 1784.
[Thrale 1775/1932]

Vigée-Lebrun, Marie-Louise-Élisabeth (1755–1842). One of the most talented and successful female painters of her time, known for her portraits of European nobility and royalty. She served as official portraitist to Queen Marie-Antoinette, of whom she painted more than twenty portraits. In 1783 she became a member of the French Académie Royale de Peinture et de Sculpture. During the French Revolution she left France and traveled abroad, working in exile in Italy and Austria and also in Russia, where she painted members of Catherine the Great's family before returning to Paris in 1801. Toward the end of her life she wrote her reminiscences, *Souvenirs de ma vie*, which were first published in 1835–37.
[Vigée-Lebrun 1834–35/1904]

Walpole, Horace, fourth Earl of Orford (1717–1797). The youngest son of the powerful Whig minister Robert Walpole, he was a member of Parliament and a man of letters who maintained a prolific and often witty correspondence with friends and acquaintances both in England and in France. Walpole is perhaps best remembered today in connection with Strawberry Hill, the Gothic Revival villa at Twickenham that he built and remodeled over a period of nearly thirty years and where he kept his art and book collections.
[Walpole 1937–83]

Watin, Jean-Félix (b. 1728). French shopkeeper, expert on colors, and author of a very popular and often republished manual on paints and varnishes.
[Watin 1772 and Watin 1778/1975]

Young, Arthur (1741–1820). Gentleman farmer and writer on agriculture and agricultural and social reform. He has been called a pioneer of social statistics. He toured both England and Ireland and made several lengthy trips to the Continent. While in France in 1787 to 1789, he observed the changing political and social climate there and documented it in a book written "with a view of ascertaining the cultivation, wealth, resources, and national prosperity, of the kingdom of France."
[Young 1792]

Bibliography

Over the years, numerous articles, several handbooks, and a few catalogues have been devoted to the Museum's galleries of European decorative arts and to different aspects of the decorative arts collections. Since this volume is built on their legacy, many of them are listed in the bibliography below. A few of the publications most relevant to the subject of this book are singled out for mention here.

An important early work dating to 1925 was *The Pierpont Morgan Wing: A Handbook*, by Joseph Breck and Meyric R. Rogers. Documenting the many wonderful treasures formerly on display in the Morgan Wing, the volume was republished in 1929. Following the removal of the European decorative arts galleries to a different part of the building, the November 1954 issue of the Museum's *Bulletin* was devoted in its entirety to the new installation. Titled *The Galleries of European Decorative Art and Period Rooms, Chiefly XVII and XVIII Century*, the text was written by Preston Remington, then Curator of Renaissance and Modern Art. In 1964 Associate Curator Edith A. Standen, best known for her extensive research on European tapestries and textiles, published *Guide to the Collections: Western European Arts*, a second printing of which appeared three years later. Neither Remington's nor Standen's publication focused exclusively on the French rooms or art objects made in France.

Documenting the incomparable 1958 gift of European decorative arts by the Samuel H. Kress Foundation to the Museum, a thoroughly researched catalogue of the Kress collection written by Carl Christian Dauterman, James Parker, and Edith A. Standen appeared in 1964. Two years later Dauterman and Francis J. B. Watson compiled comprehensive multivolume catalogues of the Wrightsman decorative arts collections, and they are still valuable scholarly works today. Those Wrightsman catalogues, however, not only are out of print and therefore difficult to find but also include numerous pieces that are not part of the Museum's holdings.

James Parker, who oversaw the installation of most of the European decorative arts galleries during his long tenure at the Museum, wrote several informative articles on the expansion of the French rooms, including "The Wrightsman Rooms: A Magnificent Donation" in *Connoisseur* for April 1970 and "The French Eighteenth-Century Rooms in the Newly Re-opened Wrightsman Galleries" in the November 1977 issue of *Apollo*. In 1979, with Associate Curator Clare Le Corbeiller, Parker coauthored the first guidebook to the Wrightsman Galleries. Invaluable in its time, it has long been out of print.

In honor of the installation of the Louis XIV–style bedchamber, the Spring 1989 issue of the *Bulletin* was dedicated to French decorative arts during the reign of the Sun King. Also important to mention here is a book published in 1996, *Period Rooms in The Metropolitan Museum of Art*, to which Parker, then curator emeritus, contributed the text for all but one of the French rooms.

Abbott 2006
James Archer Abbott. *Jansen*. Edited by Mitchell Owens. New York, 2006.

J. Adams and A. Adams 1774–83/1970
John Adams and Abigail Adams. *Familiar Letters of John Adams and His Wife Abigail Adams, during the Revolution, with a Memoir of Mrs. Adams*. [Correspondence for the years 1774–83.] Edited by Charles Francis Adams. Freeport, N.Y., 1970.

W. H. Adams 2003
William Howard Adams. *Gouverneur Morris: An Independent Life*. New Haven, 2003.

Alcouffe, Dion-Tenenbaum, and Mabille 2004
Daniel Alcouffe, Anne Dion-Tenenbaum, and Gérard Mabille. *Gilt Bronzes in the Louvre*. Translated by Ann Sautier-Greening. Dijon, 2004.

Alexander 1964
Edward P. Alexander. "Artistic and Historical Period Rooms." *Curator* (American Museum of Natural History) 7, no. 4 (1964), pp. 263–81.

Argenson 1857–58
René-Louis de Voyer de Paulmy, marquis d'Argenson. *Mémoires et journal inédit du marquis d'Argenson*. Edited by Charles-Marc-René de Voyer, marquis d'Argenson. 5 vols. Paris, 1857–58.

Baillio 1988
Joseph Baillio. "Une Artiste méconnue: Rose Adélaïde Ducreux." *L'Oeil*, no. 399 (October 1988), pp. 20–27.

Baillio 1989
Joseph Baillio. *The Winds of Revolution*. Exh. cat. Wildenstein and Company, 1989. New York, 1989.

Balsan 1952
Consuelo Vanderbilt Balsan. *The Glitter and the Gold*. New York, 1952.

Baulez 1985
Christian Baulez. "Le Choix du citoyen Alcan." In *Drouot, 1984–1985: L'Art et les enchères*, pp. 149–51. Paris, 1985.

Baulez 1986
Christian Baulez. "Pierre Gouthière (1732–1813)." In Ottomeyer and Pröschel 1986, vol. 2, pp. 561–642.

Baulez 1992
Christian Baulez. "Sèvres: Commandes et achats de Madame du Barry." *L'Estampille/ L'Objet d'art*, no. 257 (April 1992), pp. 34–53.

Baulez 2001
Christian Baulez. "Das *grand cabinet intérieur* von Marie-Antoinette: Dekor, Mobiliar und Sammlungen." In Monika Kopplin, *Japanische Lacke: Die Sammlung der Königin Marie-Antoinette*, pp. 28–41. Exh. cat. Musée National des Châteaux de Versailles et de Trianon and Museum für Lackkunst, Münster, 2001–2. Munich, 2001.

Baulez and Ledoux-Lebard 1981
Christian Baulez and Denise Ledoux-Lebard. *Il Mobile francese dal Luigi XVI all'Art Déco*. Quaderni dell'antiquariato. Collana di arti decorative 7. Milan, 1981.

Baumeister 2005
Mechthild Baumeister. "A Seventeenth-Century Parisian Ebony Cabinet Restored by Herter Brothers. Part One." WAG Postprints (Wood Artifacts Group, American Institute of Conservation). Minneapolis, Minn., 2005.

Baumeister et al. 2009
Mechthild Baumeister, Adriana Rizzo, Melanie Brussat, Erika Sanchez Goodwillie, and Batyah Shtrum. "A Re-evaluation of Three Period Rooms in the Wrightsman Galleries at The Metropolitan Museum of Art in New York." In *Architectural Finishes in the Built Environment*, edited by Mary A. Jablonski and Catherine R. Matsen, pp. 201–16. London, 2009.

Bennett and Sargentson 2008
Shelley Bennett and Carolyn Sargentson, eds. *French Art of the Eighteenth Century at the Huntington*. New Haven, 2008.

Bentley 1776/1977
Thomas Bentley. *Journal of a Visit to Paris, 1776*. Edited by Peter France. Brighton, 1977.

Berry 1783–1852/1866
Mary Berry. *Extracts of the Journals and Correspondence of Miss Berry, from the Year 1783 to 1852*. Edited by Theresa Lewis. 3 vols. 2nd ed. London, 1866.

Bimbenet-Privat 2002
Michèle Bimbenet-Privat. *Les Orfèvres et l'orfèvrerie de Paris au XVIIᵉ siècle*. 2 vols. Paris, 2002.

Blondel 1771–77
Jacques-François Blondel. *Cours d'architecture; ou, Traité de la décoration, distribution & construction des bâtiments*. 6 vols. Paris, 1771–77.

Boigne 1781–1830/1907–8
Louise-Éléonore-Charlotte-Adélaïde d'Osmond, comtesse de Boigne. *Memoirs of the Comtesse de Boigne*. [Memoirs of the years 1781–1830.] Edited by Charles Nicoullaud. 3 vols. New York, 1907–8.

Bollea 1942
Luigi Cesare Bollea. *Lorenzo Pecheux: Maestro di pittura nella R. Accademia delle Belle Arti di Torino*. Collezione "La R. Accademia Albertina delle Belle Arti" 8. Turin, 1942.

Breck and Rogers 1925
Joseph Breck and Meyric R. Rogers. *The Pierpont Morgan Wing: A Handbook*. The Metropolitan Museum of Art. New York, 1925. [2nd ed., 1929.]

Bremer-David forthcoming
Charissa Bremer-David. "The Tapestry Patronage of Madame de Montespan and Her Family." In *Tapestry in the Baroque: Threads of Splendor—A Symposium*. Edited by Thomas P. Campbell and Elizabeth A. H. Cleland. Forthcoming.

Brice 1687
Germain Brice. *A New Description of Paris: Containing a Particular Account of All the Churches, Palaces, Monasteries . . . with All Other Remarkable Matters in That Great and Famous City*. London, 1687.

Brunet and Préaud 1978
Marcelle Brunet and Tamara Préaud. *Sèvres: Des origines à nos jours*. Fribourg, 1978.

Campan 1823
Jeanne-Louise-Henriette Campan, née Henriette Genet or Genest. *Memoirs of the Private Life of Marie Antoinette, Queen of France and Navarre, to Which Are Added, Recollections, Sketches, and Anecdotes, Illustrative of the Reigns of Louis XIV., Louis XV., and Louis XVI.* 2 vols. London, 1823.

Carlier 2006
Yves Carlier. *Le Boudoir de Marie-Antoinette à Fontainebleau*. Paris and Fontainebleau, 2006.

Chambers 1759
William Chambers. *A Treatise on Civil Architecture, in Which the Principles of That Art Are Laid Down*. London, 1759.

Cocks and Truman 1984
Anna Somers Cocks and Charles Truman. *Renaissance Jewels, Gold Boxes, and Objets de Vertu*. The Thyssen-Bornemisza Collection. London, 1984.

Cole 1765/1931
William Cole. *A Journal of My Journey to Paris in the Year 1765*. Edited by Francis Griffin Stokes. New York, 1931.

Condamy 2008
Laurent Condamy. *Jean-Baptiste Boulard: Menuisier du Roi*. Saint-Étienne, 2008.

Constans 1995
Claire Constans. *Les Peintures*. 3 vols. Rev. ed. Musée National du Château de Versailles. Paris, 1995.

Courtin 1997
Nicolas Courtin. "Boutique, 3, quai de Bourbon." In *L'Île Saint-Louis*, edited by Béatrice de Andia and Nicolas Courtin, pp. 134–36. Collection Paris et son patri-moine. Paris, 1997.

Cradock 1828
Joseph Cradock. *Literary and Miscellaneous Memoirs*. 4 vols. London, 1828.

Daly 1870
César Daly. *Motifs historiques d'architecture et de sculpture d'ornement pour la composition et la décoration extérieure des édifices publics et privés*. 1st ser., *Choix de fragments empruntés à des monuments français, du commencement de la Renaissance à la fin du Louis XVI*. 2 vols. Paris, 1870.

Dauterman 1970
Carl Christian Dauterman. *The Wrightsman Collection*. Vol. 4, *Porcelain*. New York, 1970.

Dauterman, Parker, and Standen 1964
Carl Christian Dauterman, James Parker, and Edith Appleton Standen. *Decorative Art from the Samuel H. Kress Collection at The Metropolitan Museum of Art: The Tapestry Room from Croome Court, Furniture, Textiles, Sèvres Porcelains, and Other Objects*. New York, 1964.

Dell 1967
Theodore Dell. "The Gilt-Bronze Cartel Clocks of Charles Cressent." *Burlington Magazine* 109 (April 1967), pp. 210–17.

Dell 1992
Theodore Dell. *The Frick Collection: An Illustrated Catalogue*. Vol. 6, *Furniture and Gilt Bronzes: French*. New York, 1992.

Dennis 1960
Faith Dennis. *Three Centuries of French Domestic Silver: Its Makers and Its Marks*. 2 vols. New York, 1960.

De Piles 1743
Roger De Piles. *The Principles of Painting*. London, 1743. [Translation of *Cours de peinture par principes*. Paris, 1708.]

Dézallier d'Argenville 1757
Antoine-Nicolas Dézallier d'Argenville. *Voyage pittoresque de Paris; ou, Indication de tout ce qu'il y a de plus beau dans cette grande ville en peinture, sculpture & architecture*. 3rd ed. Paris, 1757.

***Dictionnaire de biographie française* 1933–**
Dictionnaire de biographie française. 19 vols. to date. Paris, 1933–.

Diderot 1751–72
Denis Diderot, with Jean Le Rond d'Alembert. *Encyclopédie; ou, Dictionnaire raisonné des sciences, des arts et des métiers*. 28 vols. Paris, 1751–72.

D'Orey 1991
Leonor D'Orey. *The Silver Service of the Portuguese Crown*. Lisbon, 1991.

Draper 1999
James David Draper. "Pajou and Roland." In *Augustin Pajou et ses contemporains*: *Actes du colloque organisé au Musée du Louvre par le Service Culturel les 7 et 8 novembre 1997*, edited by Guilhem Scherf, pp. 537–58. Louvre conférences et colloques. Paris, 1999.

Du Coudray 1778
Alexandre-Jacques Du Coudray. *Anecdotes of the Emperor Joseph II, during His Residence in France upon a Visit to His Sister the Present Queen of France*. 2nd ed. London, 1778.

Dufort de Cheverny 1794–95/1990
Jean-Nicolas, comte Dufort de Cheverny. *Mémoires*. [Written 1794–95.] Edited by Jean-Pierre Guicciardi. L'Histoire en mémoires. Paris, 1990.

Duvaux 1748–58/1965
Lazare Duvaux. *Livre-journal de Lazare Duvaux: Marchand-bijoutier ordinaire du Roy, 1748–1758*. Edited by Louis Courajod. 2 vols. Paris, 1965. [Reprint (facsimile) of edition published Paris, 1873.]

Eastlake 1895
Lady Elizabeth Eastlake, née Rigby. *Journals and Correspondence of Lady Eastlake*. Edited by Charles Eastlake Smith. 2 vols. London, 1895.

Edey 1982
Winthrop Edey. *French Clocks in North American Collections: The Frick Collection*. Exh. cat. Frick Collection, 1982–83. New York, 1982.

Edgcumbe 2000
Richard Edgcumbe. *The Art of the Gold Chaser in Eighteenth-Century London*. Oxford, 2000.

Eriksen and Bellaigue 1987
Svend Eriksen and Geoffrey de Bellaigue. *Sèvres Porcelain: Vincennes and Sèvres, 1740–1800*. Danish text translated by R. J. Charleston. London, 1987.

Fabian 1996
Dietrich Fabian. *Abraham und David Roentgen: Das noch aufgefundene Gesamtwerk ihrer Möbel- und Uhrenkunst in Verbindung mit der Uhrmacherfamilie Kinzing in Neuwied. Leben und Werk, Verzeichnis der Werke, Quellen*. Bad Neustadt, 1996.

Fahy and Watson 1973
Everett Fahy and Francis J. B. Watson. *The Wrightsman Collection*. Vol. 5, *Paintings, Drawings, Sculpture*. New York, 1973.

Feodorovna 1795/1903
Maria Feodorovna. "Description du Grand Palais de Pavlovsk, rédigée et écrite par la grande-duchesse Marie Féodorovna en 1795." In Alexandre Benois, *Les Trésors d'art en Russie*, vol. 3, pp. 371–82. Saint Petersburg, 1903.

***France in the Eighteenth Century* 1968**
France in the Eighteenth Century. Exh. cat. Royal Academy of Arts, 1968. London, 1968.

Fuhring 1999
Peter Fuhring. *Juste-Aurèle Meissonnier: Un Génie du Rococo, 1695–1750*. 2 vols. Turin, 1999.

Gady and Pérouse de Montclos 2005
Alexandre Gady and Jean-Marie Pérouse de Montclos, eds. *De l'esprit des villes: Nancy et l'Europe urbaine au siècle des lumières, 1720–1770*. Exh. cat. Musée des Beaux-Arts, 2005. Nancy, 2005.

Gibbon 1788–93/1966
Edward Gibbon. *Memoirs of My Life*. [Written 1788–93.] Edited by Georges A. Bonnard. London, 1966.

Gimpel 1918–39/1963
René Gimpel. *Diary of an Art Dealer*. [Written 1918–39.] Translated by John Rosenberg. New York, 1963.

González-Palacios 2003
Alvar González-Palacios. "Daguerre, Lignereux and the King of Naples's Cabinet at Caserta." *Burlington Magazine* 145 (June 2003), pp. 431–42.

Les Grands Orfèvres 1965
Les Grands Orfèvres de Louis XIII à Charles X. Preface by Jacques Helft. Collection Connaissance des arts "Grands artisans d'autrefois." Paris, 1965.

Hall 2009
Michael Hall. "The Chanteloup Box: Recycling in the Age of Luxury." In *The Duc de Choiseul: Essays in Honour of Mrs Charles Wrightsman*, pp. 54–59. Waddesdon Miscellanea 1. Waddesdon, 2009.

Harris 2007
John Harris. *Moving Rooms: The Trade in Architectural Salvages.* New Haven, 2007.

Hautecoeur 1912
Louis Hautecoeur. *L'Architecture classique à Saint-Pétersbourg à la fin du XVIIIᵉ siècle.* Paris, 1912.

Hecht 1994
Johanna Hecht. "The Stone Ghost: Two Russians in Enlightenment Paris." *Apollo* 140 (July 1994), pp. 28–35.

Hughes 1996
Peter Hughes. *The Wallace Collection: Catalogue of Furniture.* 3 vols. London, 1996.

Impey and Kisluk-Grosheide 1994
Oliver R. Impey and Daniëlle O. Kisluk-Grosheide. "The Japanese Connection: French Eighteenth-Century Furniture and Export Lacquer." *Apollo* 139 (January 1994), pp. 48–61.

Jarry 1966
Madeleine Jarry. *The Carpets of the Manufacture de la Savonnerie.* Leigh-on-Sea, 1966.

K. Johnson 2007
Ken Johnson. "Gilding the Ancien Régime." *New York Times*, November 9, 2007, sect. E, p. 44.

S. Johnson 1775/1932
Samuel Johnson. "Dr. Johnson's French Journal, 1775." In *The French Journals of Mrs. Thrale and Doctor Johnson*, edited by Moses Tyson and Henry Guppy, pp. 167–88. Manchester, 1932.

Jordan 2008
Marc-Henri Jordan. "L'Étude de l'ornement et l'art du décor." In Pierre Pinon et al., *Le Cabinet de Pierre-Adrien Pâris: Architecte, dessinateur des menus-plaisirs*, pp. 40–57. Exh. cat. Musée des Beaux-Arts et d'Archéologie, 2008–9. Besançon, 2008.

Jouin 1878
Henry Jouin. *David d'Angers: Sa Vie, son oeuvre, ses écrits et ses contemporains.* 2 vols. Paris, 1878.

Kisluk-Grosheide 1996
Daniëlle O. Kisluk-Grosheide. "The Bordeaux Room, Bordeaux, 1785." In *Period Rooms in The Metropolitan Museum of Art* 1996, pp. 127–33.

Kisluk-Grosheide 2005
Daniëlle O. Kisluk-Grosheide. "Versailles au Metropolitan Museum de New York." With a contribution by Jeffrey Munger. *Versalia: Revue de la Société des Amis de Versailles*, no. 8 (2005), pp. 66–93.

Kisluk-Grosheide 2006
Daniëlle O. Kisluk-Grosheide. "French Royal Furniture in the Metropolitan Museum." *The Metropolitan Museum of Art Bulletin*, n.s., 63, no. 3 (Winter 2006).

Kisluk-Grosheide 2009
Daniëlle O. Kisluk-Grosheide. "Peregrinations of a *Lit à la Duchesse en Impériale* by Georges Jacob." *Metropolitan Museum Journal* 44 (2009), pp. 139–61.

Kisluk-Grosheide, Koeppe, and Rieder 2006
Daniëlle O. Kisluk-Grosheide, Wolfram Koeppe, and William Rieder. *European Furniture in The Metropolitan Museum of Art: Highlights of the Collection.* New York, 2006.

Klappenbach 2001
Käthe Klappenbach. *Kronleuchter, mit Behang aus Bergkristall und Glas sowie Glasarmkronleuchter bis 1810.* Stiftung Preussische Schlösser und Gärten Berlin-Brandenburg. Berlin, 2001.

Knox 1958
Sanka Knox. "Rare Art Items Given to Museum." *New York Times*, October 20, 1958, p. 31.

Koeppe 1989
Wolfram Koeppe. "Ein Girandolenpaar des Albrecht Biller: Addenda zum Einfluss französischer Ornamentformen auf die Augsburger Goldschmiedekunst um 1700." *Jahrbuch des Museums für Kunst und Gewerbe Hamburg*, n.s., 8 (1989), pp. 63–76.

Koeppe 2008
Wolfram Koeppe, ed. *Art of the Royal Court: Treasures in Pietre Dure from the Palaces of Europe.* Exh. cat. by Wolfram Koeppe and Annamaria Giusti, with contributions by Cristina Acidini et al. The Metropolitan Museum of Art, 2008. New York, 2008.

Le Camus de Mézières 1780/1992
Nicolas Le Camus de Mézières. *Le Génie de l'architecture; ou, L'Analogie de cet art avec nos sensations.* Paris, 1780. 1992 ed.: *The Genius of Architecture; or, The Analogy of That Art with Our Sensations.* Translated by David Britt. Santa Monica, Calif., 1992.

Le Corbeiller 1966
Clare Le Corbeiller. *European and American Snuff Boxes, 1730–1830.* New York, 1966.

Le Corbeiller 1977a
Clare Le Corbeiller. "Craftsmanship and Elegance in Eighteenth-Century French Silver." *Apollo* 106 (November 1977), pp. 396–401.

Le Corbeiller 1977b
Clare Le Corbeiller. *Gold Boxes: The Wrightsman Collection.* The Metropolitan Museum of Art. New York, 1977.

Le Corbeiller 1994
Clare Le Corbeiller. "Whimsy and Sobriety: Rococo Butterflies and Neo-Classical Porcelain." *Apollo* 139 (January 1994), pp. 25–27.

Lefuel 1923
Hector Lefuel. *Georges Jacob: Ébéniste du XVIIIᵉ siècle.* Paris, 1923.

Lister 1699
Martin Lister. *A Journey to Paris in the Year 1698.* London, 1699.

Lough 1987
John Lough. *France on the Eve of Revolution: British Travellers' Observations, 1763–1788.* Chicago, 1987.

Louis XV 1974
Louis XV: Un Moment de la perfection de l'art français. Exh. cat. Hôtel de la Monnaie, 1974. Paris, 1974.

Lunsingh Scheurleer 2005
Theodoor H. Lunsingh Scheurleer. *Pierre Gole: Ébéniste de Louis XIV.* Dijon, 2005.

Luynes 1735–58/1860–65
Charles-Philippe d'Albert, duc de Luynes. *Mémoires du duc de Luynes sur la cour de Louis XV (1735–1758).* Edited by Louis Dussieux and Eudoxe Soulié. 17 vols. Paris, 1860–65.

Marie-Antoinette 2008
Marie-Antoinette. Exh. cat. Galeries Nationales du Grand Palais, 2008. Paris, 2008.

Masterpieces of Fifty Centuries 1970
Masterpieces of Fifty Centuries. Introduction by Kenneth Clark. Exh. cat. The Metropolitan Museum of Art, 1970–71. New York, 1970.

Mémoires secrets 1786
Mémoires secrets pour servir à l'histoire de la République des Lettres en France. Vol. 26 [*année* 1784]. London, 1786.

Mercier 1781–88/1999
Louis-Sébastien Mercier. *Panorama of Paris: Selections from Le Tableau de Paris.* [Selections from editions of 1781–88.] Edited by Jeremy D. Popkin. University Park, Pa., 1999.

Mercier 1782–83
Louis-Sébastien Mercier. *Tableau de Paris.* New ed. 8 vols. Amsterdam, 1782–83.

Mercy-Argenteau 1770–80/1874
Marie-Antoinette: Correspondance secrète entre Marie-Thérèse et le c^te de Mercy-Argenteau, avec les lettres de Marie-Thérèse et de Marie-Antoinette. [Correspondence for the years 1770–80.] Edited by Alfred Ritter von Arneth and Auguste Geffroy. 3 vols. Paris, 1874.

Metropolitan Museum of Art 1975
The Metropolitan Museum of Art. *Notable Acquisitions, 1965–1975.* New York, 1975.

Metropolitan Museum of Art 1984
The Metropolitan Museum of Art. *Notable Acquisitions, 1983–1984.* New York, 1984.

Metropolitan Museum of Art 1986
The Metropolitan Museum of Art. *Recent Acquisitions: A Selection, 1985–1986.* New York, 1986.

Metropolitan Museum of Art 1987
The Metropolitan Museum of Art. *Recent Acquisitions: A Selection, 1986–1987.* New York, 1987.

Meyer 1990
Daniel Meyer. "A Chimneypiece from Saintonge." *Metropolitan Museum Journal* 25 (1990), pp. 27–32.

Montagu 1985
Jennifer Montagu. *Alessandro Algardi.* 2 vols. New Haven, 1985.

Morris 1789–93/1939
Gouverneur Morris. *A Diary of the French Revolution by Gouverneur Morris, 1752–1816, Minister to France during the Terror.* [Written 1789–93.] Edited by Beatrix Cary Davenport. 2 vols. Boston, 1939.

"New Wing of the Metropolitan Museum" 1910
"The Opening of the New Wing of the Metropolitan Museum." *New York Times,* March 13, 1910, p. 14.

Norberg 2007
Kathryn Norberg. "Goddesses of Taste: Courtesans and Their Furniture in Late-Eighteenth-Century Paris." In *Furnishing the Eighteenth Century: What Furniture Can Tell Us about the European and American Past,* edited by Dena Goodman and Kathryn Norberg, pp. 97–114. New York, 2007.

Nordhoff and Reimer 1994
Claudia Nordhoff and Hans Reimer. *Jakob Philipp Hackert, 1737–1807: Verzeichnis seiner Werke.* 2 vols. Acta Humaniora. Berlin, 1994.

Northumberland 1752–74/1926
Elizabeth Seymour Percy, Duchess of Northumberland. *The Diaries of a Duchess: Extracts from the Diaries of the First Duchess of Northumberland (1716–1776).* [Extracts for the years 1752–74.] Edited by James Greig. London, 1926.

Nouvelle Biographie générale 1852–66/1963–69
Nouvelle Biographie générale depuis les temps les plus reculés jusqu'à 1850–60. 46 vols. Copenhagen, 1963–69. [Reprint (facsimile) of edition published Paris, 1852–66.]

Nützliches Adress und Reisebuch 1792
Nützliches Adress und Reisebuch; oder, Archiv des nöthigsten Kentnisse von Wien für reisende Fremde und Inländer. Vienna, 1792.

Oberkirch 1789/1970
Henriette Louise de Waldner de Freundstein, baronne d'Oberkirch. *Mémoires de la baronne d'Oberkirch sur la cour de Louis XVI et la société française avant 1789.* [Written 1789.] Edited by Suzanne Burkard. Paris, 1970.

Orléans 1661–1722/1924–25
Élisabeth-Charlotte, Princess Palatine and duchesse d'Orléans. *The Letters of Madame: The Correspondence of Elizabeth-Charlotte of Bavaria, Princess Palatine, Duchess of Orléans, called "Madame" at the Court of King Louis XIV.* [Correspondence for the years 1661–1722.] Translated and edited by Gertrude Scott Stevenson. 2 vols. London, 1924–25.

Orléans 1672–1722/1970
Élisabeth-Charlotte, Princess Palatine and duchesse d'Orléans. *Letters from Liselotte, Elisabeth Charlotte, Princess Palatine and Duchess of Orléans, 'Madame', 1652–1722.* [Correspondence for the years 1672–1722.] Edited by Maria Kroll. London, 1970.

Ostergard 2001
Derek E. Ostergard, ed. *William Beckford, 1760–1844: An Eye for the Magnificent.* Exh. cat. Bard Graduate Center for Studies in the Decorative Arts, Design and Culture, New York, 2001–2. New Haven, 2001.

Ottomeyer and Pröschel 1986
Hans Ottomeyer and Peter Pröschel. *Vergoldete Bronzen: Die Bronzearbeiten des Spätbarock und Klassizismus.* With contributions by Jean-Dominique Augarde et al. 2 vols. Munich, 1986.

Pallot 1987
Bill G. B. Pallot. *L'Art du siège au XVIIIe siècle en France.* Paris, 1987. [English ed.: *The Art of the Chair in Eighteenth Century France.* Paris, 1989.]

Pallot 1993
Bill G. B. Pallot. *Furniture Collections in the Louvre*. Vol. 2, *Chairs and Consoles (Menuiserie), Seventeenth and Eighteenth Centuries*. Dijon, 1993.

Pallot 1995
Bill G. B. Pallot. "Sur les traces du 4ᵉ fauteuil de la duchesse de Parme." *L'Estampille/L'Objet d'art*, no. 291 (May 1995), pp. 58–66.

Parker 1960a
James Parker. "Other Decorative Objects." *The Metropolitan Museum of Art Bulletin*, n.s., 18, no. 9 (May 1960), pp. 296–308. [Issue titled *The Kress Galleries of French Decorative Arts*.]

Parker 1960b
James Parker. "A Royal French Clock." *The Metropolitan Museum of Art Bulletin*, n.s., 18, no. 6 (February 1960), pp. 193–201.

Parker 1966
James Parker. "French Eighteenth-Century Furniture Depicted on Canvas." *The Metropolitan Museum of Art Bulletin*, n.s., 24, no. 5 (January 1966), pp. 177–92.

Parker 1969
James Parker. "The Hôtel de Varengeville Room and the Room from the Palais Paar: A Magnificent Donation." *The Metropolitan Museum of Art Bulletin*, n.s., 28, no. 3 (November 1969), pp. 129–46.

Parker 1970
James Parker. "The Wrightsman Rooms: A Magnificent Donation." *Connoisseur* 173 (April 1970), pp. 292–97.

Parker 1973
James Parker. "Eighteenth-Century France Recreated in the 'Cold, Barbarous Country': The Tapestry Room from the Bernstorff Palace, Copenhagen." *Burlington Magazine* 115 (June 1973), pp. 367–73.

Parker 1977
James Parker. "The French Eighteenth-Century Rooms in the Newly Re-opened Wrightsman Galleries." *Apollo* 106 (November 1977), pp. 376–95.

Parker 1996a
James Parker. "The Cabris Room, Grasse, 1775–72." In *Period Rooms in The Metropolitan Museum of Art* 1996, pp. 107–15.

Parker 1996b
James Parker. "The Crillon Room, Paris, 1777–80." In *Period Rooms in The Metropolitan Museum of Art* 1996, pp. 117–25.

Parker 1996c
James Parker. "The Paar Room, Vienna, 1765–72." In *Period Rooms in The Metropolitan Museum of Art* 1996, pp. 87–105.

Parker 1996d
James Parker. "The Tessé Room, Paris, 1768–72." In *Period Rooms in The Metropolitan Museum of Art* 1996, pp. 97–105.

Parker 1996e
James Parker. "The Varengeville Room, Paris, 1736–52." In *Period Rooms in The Metropolitan Museum of Art* 1996, pp. 77–85.

Parker and Le Corbeiller 1979
James Parker and Clare Le Corbeiller. *A Guide to the Wrightsman Galleries at The Metropolitan Museum of Art*. New York, 1979.

Parker et al. 1989
James Parker, Alice M. Zrebiec, Jessie McNab, Clare Le Corbeiller, and Clare Vincent. "French Decorative Arts during the Reign of Louis XIV, 1654–1715." *The Metropolitan Museum of Art Bulletin*, n.s., 46, no. 4 (Spring 1989).

Peckham 1788
Harry Peckham. *A Tour through Holland, Dutch Brabant, the Austrian Netherlands, and Part of France: In Which Is Included a Description of Paris and Its Environs . . . .* 4th ed. London, 1788. [1st ed., 1772.]

Périté and Brière 1908
André Périté and Gaston Brière. *Collections Georges Hoentschel*. 4 vols. Paris, 1908.

Period Rooms in The Metropolitan Museum of Art 1996
Period Rooms in The Metropolitan Museum of Art. With contributions by Amelia Peck et al. New York, 1996.

Pons 1986
Bruno Pons. *De Paris à Versailles, 1699–1736: Les Sculpteurs ornemanistes parisiens et l'art décoratif des Bâtiments du Roi*. Strasbourg, 1986.

Pons 1995
Bruno Pons. *French Period Rooms, 1650–1800: Rebuilt in England, France and the Americas*. Dijon, 1995.

Popkin and Fort 1998
Jeremy D. Popkin and Bernadette Fort, eds. *The "Mémoires Secrets" and the Culture of Publicity in Eighteenth-Century France*. Histoire de la presse 1. Oxford, 1998.

Posner 1990
Donald Posner. "Mme. de Pompadour as a Patron of the Visual Arts." *Art Bulletin* 72, no. 1 (March 1990), pp. 74–105.

Pradère 2003
Alexandre Pradère. *Charles Cressent: Sculpteur, ébéniste du Régent*. Dijon, 2003.

Préaud and d'Albis 1991
Tamara Préaud and Antoine d'Albis. *La Porcelaine de Vincennes*. Paris, 1991.

Raggio 1967
Olga Raggio. "Two Great Portraits by Lemoyne and Pigalle." *The Metropolitan Museum of Art Bulletin*, n.s., 25, no. 6 (February 1967), pp. 219–29.

Raggio 1989
Olga Raggio. "Introduction." In Parker et al. 1989, pp. 1–9.

Raggio 1991
Olga Raggio. "New Galleries for French and Italian Sculpture at The Metropolitan Museum of Art." *Gazette des beaux-arts*, 6th ser., 118 (December 1991), pp. 231–52.

"Recent Acquisitions" 1990
"Recent Acquisitions: A Selection, 1989–1990." *The Metropolitan Museum of Art Bulletin*, n.s., 48, no. 2 (Fall 1990).

"Recent Acquisitions" 1998
"Recent Acquisitions: A Selection, 1997–1998." *The Metropolitan Museum of Art Bulletin*, n.s., 56, no. 2 (Fall 1998).

"Recent Acquisitions" 2000
"Recent Acquisitions: A Selection, 1999–2000." *The Metropolitan Museum of Art Bulletin*, n.s., 58, no. 2 (Fall 2000).

"Recent Acquisitions" 2007
"Recent Acquisitions: A Selection, 2006–2007." *The Metropolitan Museum of Art Bulletin*, n.s., 65, no. 2 (Fall 2007).

Reif 1960
Rita Reif. "Porcelains Are Meant for Window Shoppers." *New York Times*, May 5, 1960, p. 31.

Reif 1973
Rita Reif. "It's Almost Like Being at a Palace in France." *New York Times*, December 10, 1973.

Remington 1924
Preston Remington. "A Louis XVI Bed." *Bulletin of The Metropolitan Museum of Art* 19, no. 1 (January 1924), pp. 6–8.

Remington 1931
Preston Remington. "An Ebony Cabinet of the Seventeenth Century." *Bulletin of The Metropolitan Museum of Art* 26, no. 10 (October 1931), pp. 232–36.

Remington 1943
Preston Remington. "A Room from the Hôtel de Tessé." *The Metropolitan Museum of Art Bulletin*, n.s., 1, no. 6 (February 1943), pp. 189–95.

Remington 1954
Preston Remington. "The Galleries of European Decorative Art and Period Rooms, Chiefly XVII and XVIII Century." *The Metropolitan Museum of Art Bulletin*, n.s., 13, no. 2 (November 1954), pp. 65–71.

Rieder 1994
William Rieder. "'B.V.R.B.' at the Met." *Apollo* 139 (January 1994), pp. 33–40.

Rieder 2002
William Rieder. "A Royal Commode and Secretaire by Riesener." *Furniture History* 38 (2002), pp. 83–96.

Robinson 1907
Edward Robinson. "The Hoentschel Collection." *Bulletin of The Metropolitan Museum of Art* 2, no. 6 (June 1907), pp. 93–99.

Robinson 1910
Edward Robinson. "The New Wing." In Robinson et al. 1910, pp. 5–7.

Robinson et al. 1910
Edward Robinson, W. R. Valentiner, Joseph Breck, and Garret C. Pier. "The Metropolitan Museum of Art: The Wing of Decorative Arts." *Bulletin of The Metropolitan Museum of Art* 5, no. 3 (March 1910), suppl.

Rogers 1921
Meyric R. Rogers. "A Louis XV Paneled Room." *Bulletin of The Metropolitan Museum of Art* 16, no. 4 (April 1921), pp. 72–76.

Rogers and Breck 1923
Meyric R. Rogers and Joseph Breck. "Three Louis XVI Rooms." *Bulletin of The Metropolitan Museum of Art* 18, no. 12 (December 1923), pp. 267–72.

Ronfort 1986a
Jean-Nérée Ronfort. "André-Charles Boulle: Die Bronzearbeiten und seine Werkstatt im Louvre." In Ottomeyer and Pröschel 1986, vol. 2, pp. 459–520.

Ronfort 1986b
Jean-Nérée Ronfort. "Le Mobilier royal à l'époque de Louis XIV, 1685: Versailles et le bureau du roi." *L'Estampille*, no. 191 (April 1986), pp. 44–51.

Roubo 1769–75
André-Jacob Roubo. *L'Art du menuisier.* 4 vols. Paris, 1769–75. [Reprint (facsimile ed.), Paris, 1977.]

Rubinstein-Bloch 1930
Stella Rubinstein-Bloch, comp. *Catalogue of the Collection of George and Florence Blumenthal, New-York.* Vol. 5, *Paintings, Drawings, Sculptures, XVIIIth Century.* Paris, 1930.

Savill 1988
Rosalind Savill. *The Wallace Collection: Catalogue of Sèvres Porcelain.* 3 vols. London, 1988.

Scherf 2008a
Guilhem Scherf. "*Apollon et les Arts* par André Brenet (Paris, vers 1734–après 1792)." Newsletter of the Département des Sculptures, Musée du Louvre, Paris, 2008.

Scherf 2008b
Guilhem Scherf. *Houdon at the Louvre: Masterworks of the Enlightenment.* Translated by Jane Marie Todd. Exh. cat. High Museum of Art, Atlanta, and Denver Art Museum, 2008–9. Paris and Atlanta, 2008.

Serrette 2009
Renaud Serrette. "From Madame de Pompadour to Chanteloup, by Way of the Duc of Penthièvre: A Set of Two *Bergères* and Six Chairs at Waddesdon Manor." In *The Duc de Choiseul: Essays in Honour of Mrs Charles Wrightsman*, pp. 60–71. Waddesdon Miscellanea 1. Waddesdon, 2009.

Sévigné 1647–96/1927
Marie de Rabutin-Chantal, marquise de Sévigné. *The Letters of Madame de Sévigné.* [Correspondence for the years 1647–96.] Introduction by A. Edward Newton. 7 vols. Philadelphia, 1927.

Sherrill 1996
Sarah B. Sherrill. *Carpets and Rugs of Europe and America.* New York, 1996.

Smollett 1766/1969
Tobias George Smollett. *Travels through France and Italy.* London, 1766. New ed.: Introduction by James Morris. Travellers' Classics 11. Fontwell, Sussex, 1969.

Smythe 1770–80/1902
Lillian C. Smythe. *The Guardian of Marie Antoinette: Letters from the Comte de Mercy-Argenteau, Austrian Ambassador to the Court of Versailles, to Marie Thérèse, Empress of Austria, 1770–1780.* 2 vols. New York, 1902.

Snowman 1966
A. Kenneth Snowman. *Eighteenth Century Gold Boxes of Europe.* London, 1966.

Standen 1951
Edith Appleton Standen. "The Roi Soleil and Some of His Children." *The Metropolitan Museum of Art Bulletin*, n.s., 9, no. 5 (January 1951), pp. 133–41.

Standen 1964
Edith Appleton Standen. *Guide to the Collections: Western European Arts.* New York, 1964.

Standen 1985
Edith Appleton Standen. *European Post-Medieval Tapestries and Related Hangings in The Metropolitan Museum of Art.* 2 vols. New York, 1985.

Streeter 1985
Colin Streeter. "Two Carved Reliefs by Aubert Parent." *J. Paul Getty Museum Journal* 13 (1985), pp. 53–66.

Swinburne 1774–1803/1900
Henry Swinburne. *Letters Written at the End of the Eighteenth Century.* [Correspondence for the years 1774–1803.] Edited by Charles White. 2 vols. Secret Memoirs of the Courts of Europe 9, 10. Philadelphia, 1900.

Taylor 1957
Francis Henry Taylor. *Pierpont Morgan as Collector and Patron, 1837–1913.* New York, 1957.

Thicknesse 1768
Philip Thicknesse. *Useful Hints to Those Who Make the Tour of France, in a Series of Letters, Written from That Kingdom.* London, 1768.

Thrale 1775/1932
Hester Lynch Salusbury Thrale. "Mrs. Thrale's French Journal, 1775." In *The French Journals of Mrs. Thrale and Doctor Johnson,* edited by Moses Tyson and Henry Guppy, pp. 67–166. Manchester, 1932.

Verlet 1963
Pierre Verlet. *French Royal Furniture: An Historical Survey, Followed by a Study of Forty Pieces Preserved in Great Britain and the United States.* London, 1963.

Verlet 1967
Pierre Verlet. "Homage to the *Dix-Huitième.*" *Apollo* 85 (March 1967), pp. 203–13.

Verlet 1982
Pierre Verlet. *The Savonnerie: Its History. The Waddesdon Collection.* James A. de Rothschild Collection at Waddesdon Manor. Fribourg, 1982.

Verlet 1987
Pierre Verlet. *Les Bronzes dorés français du XVIIIᵉ siècle.* Paris, 1987.

Verlet 1990
Pierre Verlet. *Le Mobilier royal français.* Vol. 4, *Meubles de la couronne conservés en Europe et aux États-Unis.* 2nd ed. Paris, 1990.

Verlet 1994
Pierre Verlet. *Le Mobilier royal français.* Vol. 3, *Meubles de la couronne conservés en Angleterre et aux États-Unis.* 2nd ed. Paris, 1994.

Véron-Denise 2005
Danièle Véron-Denise. "*Vertumne et Pomone* à la Banque de France: Nouvelles Précisions sur une tenture brodée du comte de Toulouse." *Bulletin de la Société de l'Histoire de l'Art Français,* 2005 (pub. 2006), pp. 83–99.

Versailles et les tables royales en Europe 1993
Versailles et les tables royales en Europe, XVIIᵉᵐᵉ–XIXᵉᵐᵉ siècles. Exh. cat. Musée National des Châteaux de Versailles et de Trianon, 1993–94. Paris, 1993.

Vigée-Lebrun 1834–35/1904
Marie-Louise-Élisabeth Vigée-Lebrun. *Memoirs of Madame Vigée Lebrun.* [Written 1834–35.] Translated by Lionel Strachey. London, 1904.

Walker 2004
Stephanie Walker, ed. *Vasemania: Neoclassical Form and Ornament in Europe. Selections from The Metropolitan Museum of Art.* Exh. cat. by Heather Jane McCormick and Hans Ottomeyer et al. Bard Graduate Center for Studies in the Decorative Arts, Design and Culture, New York, 2004. New Haven, 2004.

Walpole 1937–83
The Yale Edition of Horace Walpole's Correspondence. Edited by W. S. Lewis et al. 48 vols. New Haven, 1937–83.

Walter Gay 1980
Walter Gay: A Retrospective. Exh. cat. Grey Art Gallery and Study Center, New York University, 1980. New York, 1980.

Watin 1772
Jean-Félix Watin. *L'Art de faire et d'employer le vernis; ou L'Art du vernisseur, auquel on a joint ceux du peintre & du doreur.* Paris, 1772.

Watin 1778/1975
Jean-Félix Watin. *L'Art du peintre, doreur et vernisseur.* New ed. Liège, 1778. Reprint (facsimile ed.), Paris, 1975.

Watson 1966a
Francis J. B. Watson. "The Choiseul Boxes." In Snowman 1966, pp. 145–58.

Watson 1966b
Francis J. B. Watson. *The Wrightsman Collection.* Vol. 1, *Furniture.* New York, 1966.

Watson 1966c
Francis J. B. Watson. *The Wrightsman Collection.* Vol. 2, *Furniture, Gilt Bronze and Mounted Porcelain, Carpets.* New York, 1966.

Watson 1969
Francis J. B. Watson. "The Craftsmanship of the *Ancien Régime.*" *Apollo* 90 (September 1969), pp. 180–89.

Watson and Dauterman 1970
Francis J. B. Watson and Carl Christian Dauterman. *The Wrightsman Collection.* Vol. 3, *Furniture, Gold Boxes; Porcelain Boxes, Silver.* New York, 1970.

Wildenstein 1915–17
Georges Wildenstein. "Un Chef-d'Oeuvre retrouvé: Le Buste de la Marquise de Pompadour par J.-B. Pigalle." *Bulletin de la Société de l'Histoire de l'Art Français,* 1915–17 (pub. 1918), pp. 65–81.

Wolvesperges 2000
Thibaut Wolvesperges. *Le Meuble français en laque au XVIIIᵉ siècle.* Brussels and Paris, 2000.

Young 1792
Arthur Young. *Travels, during the Years 1787, 1788 and 1789; Undertaken More Particularly with a View of Ascertaining the Cultivation, Wealth, Resources, and National Prosperity, of the Kingdom of France.* London, 1792.

Zafran 1983
Eric M. Zafran. *The Rococo Age: French Masterpieces of the Eighteenth Century.* Exh. cat. High Museum of Art, 1983. Atlanta, 1983.

Index

Page numbers in **boldface** refer to the main illustration of a catalogue item; page numbers in *italics* refer to all other illustrations.

Photograph Credits